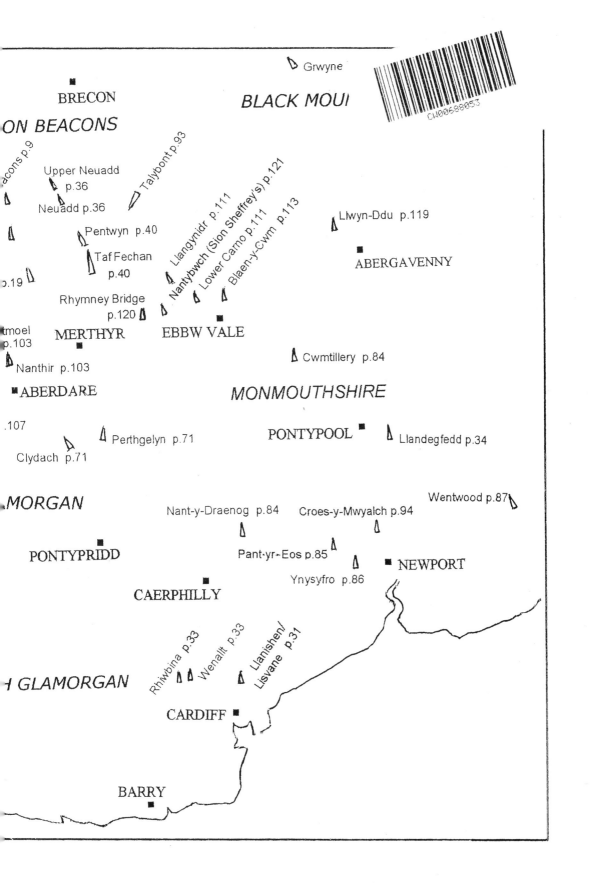

# RESERVOIR BUILDERS

## OF

# SOUTH WALES

*DAM BUILDERS IN THE AGE OF STEAM  -  BOOK SIX*

# RESERVOIR BUILDERS

## OF

# SOUTH WALES

*By*

## Harold  D  Bowtell  and  Geoffrey  Hill

## 2006

## iLs

The Industrial Locomotive Society

ISBN 0-9540726-2-6

# RESERVOIR  BUILDERS OF SOUTH WALES

## By Harold D Bowtell  and  Geoffrey Hill

First Edition,  January 2006

In the same series (all by Harold D Bowtell):
  *Reservoir Railways of Manchester and the Peak* (Oakwood Press, 1977)
  *Reservoir Railways of the Yorkshire Pennines* (Oakwood Press, 1979)
  *Lesser Railways of Bowland Forest and Craven Country* (Plateway Press, 1988)
  *Lesser Railways of the Yorkshire Dales* (Plateway Press, 1991)
  *Dam Builders' Railways from Durham's Dales to the Border* (Plateway Press, 1994)

British Library Cataloguing in Publication Data
Bowtell, Harold D., *1915-1999*
  Reservoir Builders of South Wales.
  I. Title II.  Hill, Geoffrey, *1943-*
  385.0942

### ISBN 0-9540726-2-6

© Geoffrey Hill and the Industrial Locomotive Society  2006

Cover illustration, painted by Barry C Lane, depicts the 'Paddy Mail' (workman's train) of 1912 crossing the 50ft high Hepste Viaduct (*see page 58*) during the construction of the Ystradfellte Reservoir by the contractor Morrison and Mason Ltd.

Printed in Great Britain by *The Amadeus Press*,  Cleckheaton,  West Yorkshire  BD19 4TQ
    Web site:  www.amadeuspress.co.uk      Fax: 01274 863211      Telephone: 01274 863210

Produced and designed for the Society by R W Miller.

## Published by the Industrial Locomotive Society
Web site:  www.industrial-loco.org.uk
Hon. Publications Officer: D R Embling, 77 Station Crescent, Rayleigh, Essex, SS6 8AR
e-mail:  david.embling@btconnect.com

# Contents

## LIST OF MAPS AND PLANS

*The special last train from Abergavenny to Merthyr and return, organized by the Stephenson Locomotive Society, calls at Brynmawr (1,160 feet above sea level) for the locomotives to take water on the outward journey on 5 January 1958. A few of the many spectators that day can be seen on the right.*
*[Douglas Robinson]*

# *Introduction*

The spectacular group of summits known as the Brecon Beacons approach 3,000ft in height and dominate a wide panorama of magnificent mountain country. Some ten miles to the south sits Dowlais on the 1,000ft contour and a little below it is Merthyr Tydfil. These and other towns in the heads of the South Wales valleys developed with the coal and iron industries and were reached by railways, which climbed from the seaports of Cardiff, Barry and Newport up the winding and steep-sided valleys. The London and North Western Railway also reached Merthyr from Abergavenny by fearsome grades to Brynmawr and then over the valley heads by Nantybwch (nearly 1,200ft) and Rhymney Bridge; that fierce railway closed after the return from Merthyr to Abergavenny on 5 January 1958 of the Stephenson Locomotive Society's (SLS) special train, with engines 58926 (0-6-2T "Coal Tank") and 49121 (0-8-0 "Super D"). Merthyr itself is still reached by rail, but only by the former Taff Vale line, which comes up the valleys from Cardiff. Five miles north of the Beacons is the old town of Brecon, now entirely without railways, although it was formerly served by trains of the Brecon & Merthyr, Cambrian, Midland and Neath & Brecon Railways. The N&B line closed from 15 October 1962. An SLS "last train" ran on 30 December 1962 to mark the end of the Cambrian and Midland routes and another on 2 May 1964, when the last approach - that of the B&M line over the mountains from the south - finally succumbed.

It is hoped that the text that follows, read in conjunction with the accompanying maps, will explain how the conservation and development of water supplies for industrial South Wales through the building of dams in the mountain country (and beyond in the hinterland) came about. An appreciation of the main line railways in the area, particularly those to Merthyr and Brecon in their heyday, will place in context the contractors' lines used in reservoir construction that are here identified and described.

*Cantref Reservoir in the Vale of the Taf Fawr, completed by Cardiff Corporation in 1892, looking north from the dam on 25 May 2004.*            *[Geoffrey Hill]*

*Five of the six small locomotives employed by Cardiff Corporation on the building of the Llwynon dam and reservoir (see Chapter 2), captured on film in an off-duty moment on 14 March 1923. From the left they are ABERNANT (Manning Wardle 2015 of 1921), DAN-Y-GRAIG (Manning Wardle 835 of 1882), NELSON (Kitson 1786 of 1871), CWM TAFF (Hudswell Clarke 1466 of 1921) and on the far right LLWYN-ON (Hudswell Clarke 1429 of 1920).*

*[Harold D Bowtell Collection]*

# *Preface*

This book is part of a continuation of the late Harold D Bowtell's "Dam Builders in the Age of Steam" series. Five books were published in Harold's lifetime; *Reservoir Railways of Manchester and the Peak* (Oakwood Press, 1977), *Reservoir Railways of the Yorkshire Pennines* (Oakwood, 1979), *Lesser Railways of Bowland Forest and Craven Country* (Plateway Press, 1988), *Lesser Railways of the Yorkshire Dales* (Plateway, 1991) and *Dam Builders' Railways from Durham's Dales to the Border* (Plateway, 1994).

Harold Dudley Bowtell was born in Chorlton, Manchester in August 1915. His first love was the London & North Western Railway and he was later one of five founders of the Manchester Locomotive Society in 1935. He is thought to have joined the Industrial Locomotive Society in 1948. He was also to become chairman of the north-west area of the Stephenson Locomotive Society and instigated the joint MLS/SLS railtours committee, which organised many imaginative tours, often over freight–only tracks, from 1951. Harold worked for the British Engine Insurance Company, specialising in boiler insurance, based in Manchester (and, for some years, also in Birmingham). During World War 2 he served with the Pioneer Corps but was soon transferred to the Railway Operating Division of the Royal Engineers, gaining a commission and spending much of his service in India, notably on the Assam-Bengal Railway. He lived for many years at Gatley in suburban Cheshire and on retirement in 1978 moved to Kendal, the gateway to his beloved Lake District.

At his death, on 3 February 1999 at the age of 83, Harold bequeathed to the Industrial Locomotive Society, of which he had been a distinguished member, research notes and text, compiled over more than forty years, for three more planned volumes in the "Dam Builders in the Age of Steam" series. These volumes were to cover Scotland, those areas of Lancashire not within the purview of the Bowland Forest volume, and South Wales - the subject of this book. In addition, he left a generous legacy to the Society to help it continue its aims. The Society decided that a very appropriate way of honouring Harold's memory would be to bring the three projected books to publication. So it was that eleven research folders and in excess of twenty thousand words of text were handed over to the present writer by the Society in July 2001.

Harold's South Wales draft text (a top copy and carbon copy typed in the mid 1970s) actually appeared under the header "Brecon Beacons", that being the geographical area that contained the great majority of the reservoirs considered. Grwyne Fawr Reservoir is quite clearly in the Black Mountains, but that range lies within the boundaries of the Brecon Beacons National Park, designated in 1957, so there was no great difficulty there. However, closer scrutiny showed that sometime after completing his first draft, a section covering the construction of Newport Corporation's Wentwood Reservoir was added. By no stretch of imagination could this be considered in the Brecon Beacons. Then there were a few paragraphs on the reservoirs at Maerdy in the (little) Rhondda Valley and on Cardiff's reservoir at Wenallt in the northern suburbs of that city, also outside the original geographic scope of the book.

The present writer felt that it was preferable to amend the title of the proposed book rather than to reject some of the information as being without the area of study. In support of this decision, additional, if somewhat limited, information on other South Wales reservoirs has come to light since Harold wrote his first draft, notably concerning those in and around Cardiff, Swansea and Llanelli, all well outside the Brecon Beacons. Given the extended remit, the present writer has been able to include some treatment of these additional sites with a clear conscience.

The text is now some 70 per cent longer than Harold's first draft, partly as a result of the broadening of the geographical scope outlined in the preceding paragraph, but also reflecting the great increase in researchers' knowledge of contracts and contractors' railways and locomotives over the past 30 years. Harold's text has thus been extended calling on recent material from many researchers and sources. Finally, I have edited the whole and made corrections in the light of present knowledge to what was, in fairness to Harold, intended as an early draft. Wherever possible, I have retained Harold's words as he wrote them. I hope, therefore, that I have improved the text somewhat while retaining the flavour of Harold's distinctive prose style. Where, in the text, I have referred in an editorial manner to Harold's theories concerning locomotive identities (in particular), I have referred to Harold as "HDB".

A point worth emphasizing is that the authors' interests here centre mainly on reservoir sites where railways and locomotives were used in the construction phase. The earliest known use of locomotives in the pages that follow occurred at Blaen-nant-Ddu Reservoir (see Chapter 4) where the contract was let in August 1874, and at Castell Nos Reservoir (see Chapter 8) where work started in c.1876. Many earlier reservoirs make fleeting appearances in the text; for example Newport's Ynysyfro (opened 1848), Merthyr Tydfil's Pentwyn (built 1859 - 1863) and Tredegar's Sion Sheffreys (built c.1863 - 1865 by the Tredegar Iron Company and later passing to the Urban District Council) but no locomotive use is known. The use of tramroads and horses is perhaps more likely in those early days. Neither is any serious treatment attempted in these pages of recently built reservoirs where railway use was not a feature (or is thought not to have been a feature) of the construction period. Two such sites are worth mentioning in this context. Neither West Glamorgan Water Board's 13.4 million gallon Llyn Brianne Reservoir, situated 12 miles north of Llandovery and built by George Wimpey & Company Limited between 1968 and 1972, nor Cardiff Corporation's 5.39 million gallon Llandegfedd Reservoir, east of Pontypool, opened in 1964/65, are known to have used railways although a few notes on the latter do appear in Chapter 2.

All of the reservoirs discussed in this book that were still operational at 1 April 1974 will have passed to the control of the Welsh National Water Development Authority from that date. Welsh Water plc will have become responsible for them with the advent of privatisation in 1989.

I met Harold Bowtell on a very few occasions only. One of these was particularly memorable. On July 10, 1963, a fine summer evening, the Manchester Locomotive Society and the Railway Correspondence & Travel Society (I think) had arranged a joint visit to the locomotive sheds at Newton Heath, Manchester, and Lees, at Oldham. The meeting point was Piccadilly Gardens in Manchester; (those were the days when you could drive to central Manchester at 6.30 pm and have no worries about finding a parking spot). Harold took efficient charge of allocating spare seats in cars to the "carless". I was very much a newcomer, studying in Salford nearby, hanging on the fringe of the group. Having fixed everyone else up, Harold turned to me, asked my name and then said, "Right, you come with me". So I was privileged to enjoy a ride in his famous Sunbeam Talbot 90 "soft-top".

GH, 10/2005

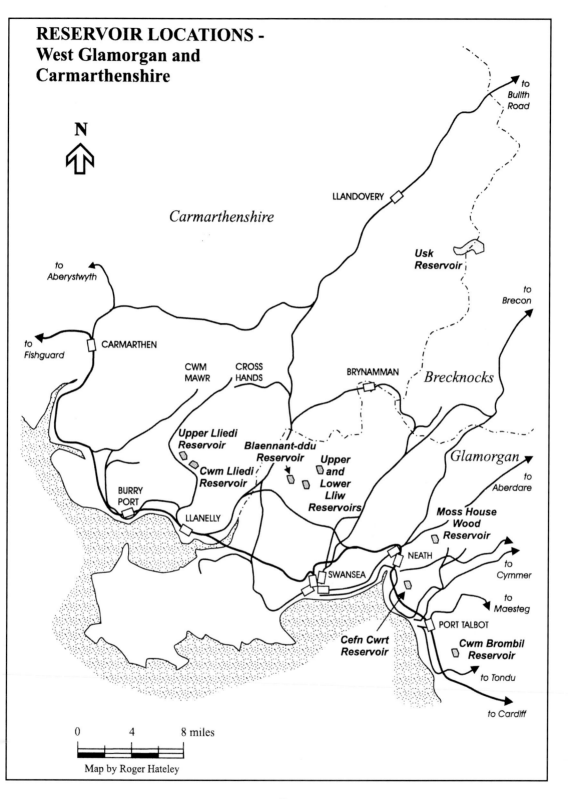

**RESERVOIR LOCATIONS -
West Glamorgan and
Carmarthenshire**

N

*to
Bullth
Road*

LLANDOVERY

*Carmarthenshire*

*Usk
Reservoir*

*to
Aberystwyth*

*to
Brecon*

*to
Fishguard*

CARMARTHEN

CWM
MAWR

CROSS
HANDS

BRYNAMMAN

*Brecknocks*

**Upper Lliedi
Reservoir**

**Blaennant-ddu
Reservoir**

**Upper
and
Lower
Lliw
Reservoirs**

*Glamorgan*

*to
Aberdare*

**Cwm Lliedi
Reservoir**

BURRY
PORT

**Moss House
Wood
Reservoir**

LLANELLY

NEATH

*to
Cymmer*

SWANSEA

*to
Maesteg*

PORT TALBOT

**Cefn Cwrt
Reservoir**

**Cwm Brombil
Reservoir**

*to Tondu*

*to Cardiff*

0      4      8 miles

Map by Roger Hateley

5

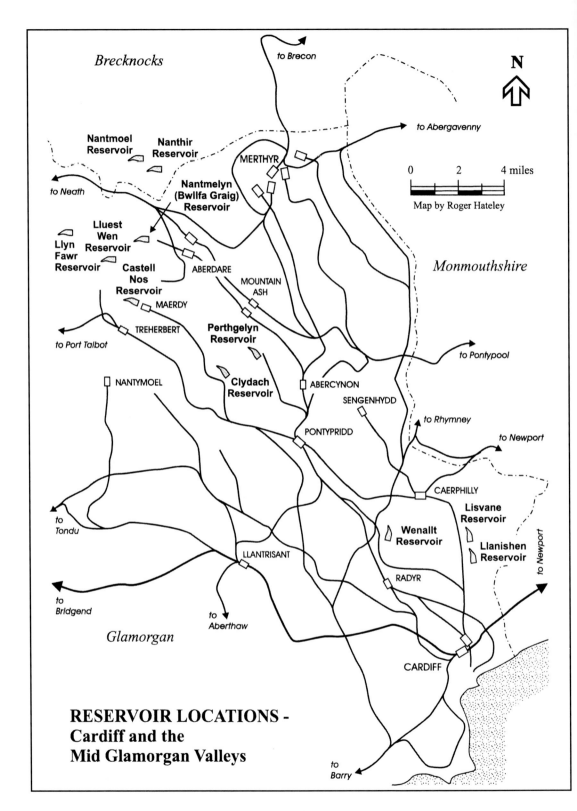

**RESERVOIR LOCATIONS –
Cardiff and the
Mid Glamorgan Valleys**

*Brecknocks*

to Brecon

to Abergavenny

N

Nantmoel
Reservoir

Nanthir
Reservoir

MERTHYR

to Neath

Nantmelyn
(Bwllfa Graig)
Reservoir

0    2    4 miles

Map by Roger Hateley

Lluest
Wen
Reservoir

Llyn
Fawr
Reservoir

Castell
Nos
Reservoir

ABERDARE

MOUNTAIN
ASH

*Monmouthshire*

MAERDY

TREHERBERT

Perthgelyn
Reservoir

to Port Talbot

to Pontypool

NANTYMOEL

Clydach
Reservoir

ABERCYNON

SENGENHYDD

PONTYPRIDD

to Rhymney

to Newport

to
Tondu

CAERPHILLY

Lisvane
Reservoir

Wenallt
Reservoir

Llanishen
Reservoir

LLANTRISANT

to Newport

RADYR

to
Bridgend

to
Aberthaw

*Glamorgan*

CARDIFF

to
Barry

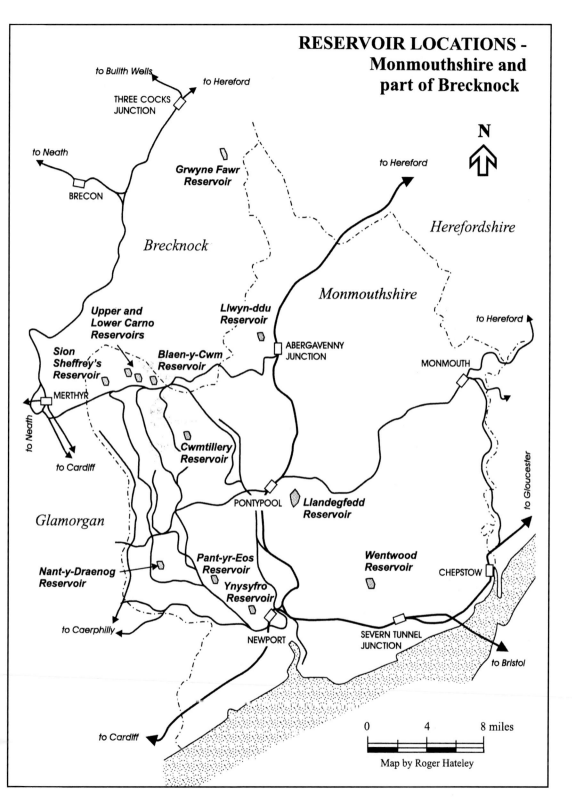

**RESERVOIR LOCATIONS –
Monmouthshire and
part of Brecknock**

N

to Builth Wells

to Hereford

THREE COCKS
JUNCTION

to Neath

*Grwyne Fawr
Reservoir*

to Hereford

*Herefordshire*

BRECON

*Brecknock*

*Monmouthshire*

*Upper and
Lower Carno
Reservoirs*

*Llwyn-ddu
Reservoir*

to Hereford

*Sion
Sheffrey's
Reservoir*

*Blaen-y-Cwm
Reservoir*

ABERGAVENNY
JUNCTION

MONMOUTH

MERTHYR

to Neath

*Cwmtillery
Reservoir*

to Cardiff

*Glamorgan*

PONTYPOOL

*Llandegfedd
Reservoir*

to Gloucester

*Nant-y-Draenog
Reservoir*

*Pant-yr-Eos
Reservoir*

*Ynysyfro
Reservoir*

*Wentwood
Reservoir*

CHEPSTOW

to Caerphilly

NEWPORT

SEVERN TUNNEL
JUNCTION

to Bristol

to Cardiff

0     4     8 miles

Map by Roger Hateley

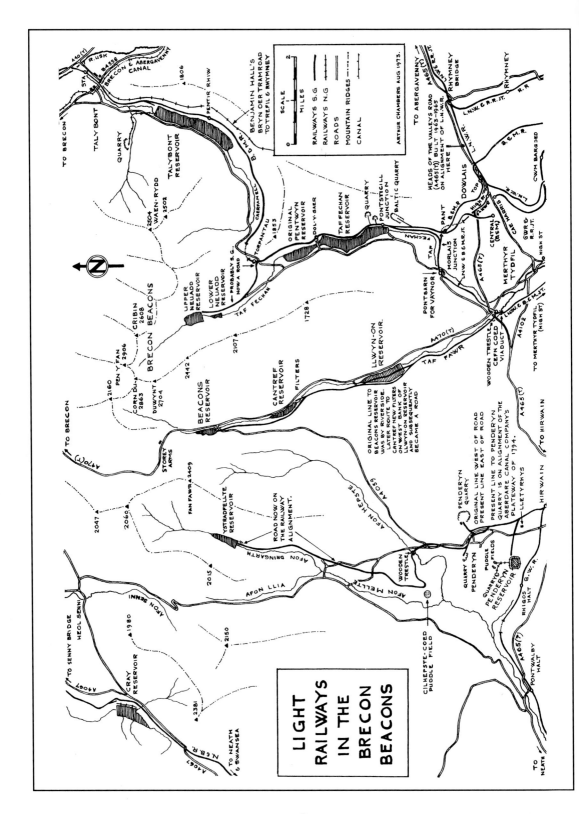

# Chapter 1

# Railways of Cardiff Corporation in the Valley of the Taf Fawr

## *Cantref and Beacons*

Perhaps not surprisingly it was the City of Cardiff that first planned major waterworks in the mountains. An Act of 1884 contemplated: -

| | |
|---|---|
| *Reservoir N°.1 - Beacons* | 160 million gallons (later 345 million gallons) with top water level at 1,340ft.   (Constructed 1894-1897). |
| *Reservoir N°. 2 - Cantref (originally Cantreff)* | 323 million gallons with top water level at 1,073ft.   (Constructed 1886-1892). |
| *Reservoir N°. 3 - Llwynon* | 670 million gallons (later 1,260 million gallons) with top water level at 854ft.   (Constructed 1910-1926). |

Access was to be by a private standard gauge railway from Cefn Coed, a village station on the LNWR/B&MR joint line out of Merthyr.  The projects were actually carried out in the order N°. 2 (Cantref, originally Cantreff), N°. 1 (Beacons) and N°. 3 (Llwynon) and the first two were under the general direction of Mr J A B Williams, the Cardiff City Water Engineer, 1881 - 1896.  Tenders for building an earth dam about 600ft long with puddle-clay core at Cantref, at grid reference SN 996153 just north of Lord Tredegar's Nant-Ddu shooting lodge, were opened in October 1885.  Household names of the day such as Pearsons, who gained repute on railway building and projects for the Admiralty, appeared but the Corporation accepted the quotation of William Jones of Neath in November 1885 - at a price much the same as that of Pearsons.  The first sod was cut on 4 May 1886 by the Mayor, at which time two miles of the proposed six-mile railway had already been constructed.  During 1886 - 1888 the contractor dug the embankment trench and put the concrete "key" in its bottom.  However, he obviously lacked funds and had insufficient pumping plant. His labour force fell off and progress became painfully slow.  On 29 October 1888, the Town Clerk took formal possession of the works and took over Jones' plant, implements and tools.  There was the usual interregnum, during which a writ was taken out, Jones v. Cardiff Corporation, claiming forcible ejection from the site of the works and repudiation of the contract.  A final settlement was agreed in June 1889, the Corporation paying £10,000 into the court the following month.

In March 1889 the tender of John Mackay of Newport for completion of the works (£89,619) was accepted.  He had earlier built Llanishen, Rhiwbina, Blackbrook and Cefn reservoirs for Cardiff Corporation (for details of the first two see Chapter 2) and had shared in building the Barry Railway, opened 1888/89.  Mackay commenced work on the Cantref project on 13 March 1889, taking over Jones' plant and bringing in more.  He appeared to set to work with a will but again difficulties and delays set in, friction at the site coming to a head in October 1890.  Then, on 8 November,

*"..... myself.....being behind hand in the completion of this work.....but what can mortal man do in the face of the horrible weather experienced all this summer and up to now? Causing the carrying out of the work to be most expensive and slow, every month's work done not paying for itself, wages of men very high, and the of a quality of labour very inferior, owing to the outlandish situation of the work and the bad weather causing men to leave every day to get into a better clime.  No sooner a gang of good serviceable men are got together than a day of two of rain disperses them; wet without, wet within becomes the sequence"*

wrote an exasperated John Mackay from Reay Villa, Bodenham Road, Hereford, to Mr Williams, the City Water Engineer, revealing some of the problems of civil engineering in the Brecon Beacons in the "nineties".

Nonetheless, Mackay soldiered on through the winter of 1890/91 and into the following summer. In February an assessment showed that he had done rather over half the work for which he contracted but his contract period of two years was to run out at 31 March 1891. On 18 March 1891, he met the Water Committee who resolved to relieve him of the contract, to settle for work done and to take possession of the plant, material, railways, quarry and clay field belonging to him or held by him for the works. This included the plant previously used by William Jones, which remained the Corporation's property. Thus the locomotive (or locomotives) of Jones and those brought by Mackay would all pass to the Corporation. Mackay accepted the Corporation's terms and finally ceased work on Saturday 13 June 1891.

Work still had to be done at Cantref and was completed by direct labour. First, Mr J T Jones acted as Manager but he had to give up through illness, and in November 1891 Mr F Orton was appointed Resident Engineer and Manager at the site. Water was first impounded on 14 September 1892 and piped to Llanishen, just north of Cardiff. The official opening was on this September day, by Alderman David Jones, JP, chairman of the city's Waterworks Committee. The name of J A B Williams appears on a plaque recording the opening but, significantly, not that of any contractors.

The railway from Cefn Coed was built by William Jones, the first contractor, on the basis of a mortgage from the Corporation and with a provision that it would in any case be taken over by the Corporation. Building of the railway started around April 1886, the upper part of the route passing through the grounds of Nant-Ddu, by permission of Lord Tredegar. By October 1886 the line had reached to within a quarter mile of the Cantref embankment site but ballasting had been delayed due to storm damage. It would be finished soon after this. The railway was valued at £3,395 in December 1888, after Jones had been turned off the job. A temporary incline "for materials" on the west side of the valley, north of the dam, was completed in June 1889. It is not clear whether at this time the "main line" ran to the top level of the projected dam, on the west side of the valley, or along the bottom of the valley, over the stream to its east side and beside Nant-Ddu Lodge to the foot of the dam. It may have been on both the upper and lower alignments, but the building of an incline suggests that either it was on the upper level and cement and masonry were lowered to the valley floor or that it was down in the valley and materials were hauled up the incline when required.

The puddle-clay field was on Cyfarthfa Works' property, near the Six Bells public house at Pen-yr-Heolgerrig. A 3ft gauge railway was used here to draw out the clay to the main line. Cyfarthfa was the huge ironworks of Crawshay Brothers, located near Merthyr and skirted by the LNWR/B&MR joint line, over which large quantities of the clay would be brought, the wagons going onto the Corporation's line at Cefn Coed for hauling up the valley to Cantref by the private locomotives. The stripping of the clay field and the haulage of traffic from it began in Mackay's time, in the spring of 1889, and it would be this that rendered imperative the acquisition of additional locomotives referred to later.

Cornish granite was used to face the weir and on the steps of the overflow channel on the west side but otherwise stone was obtained locally. The necessary quarry was opened up in Jones' era, with sidings. It was on the land of Mr Osborne Sheppard near Cefn and is presumed to be the one near the cemetery, which was also used for the later Cwm Taf reservoirs and is marked on our map of Cardiff Corporation's railway.

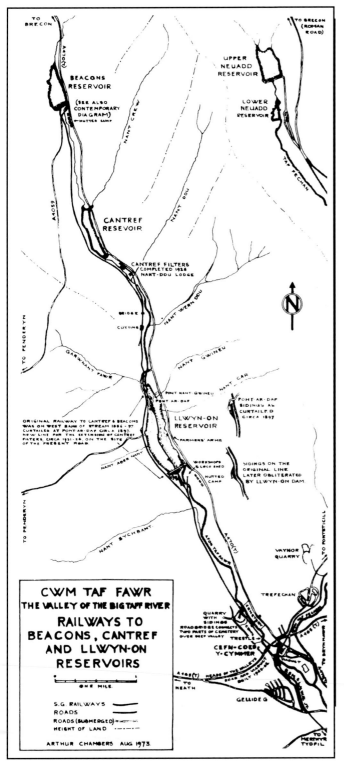

BEACONS
RESERVOIR

(SEE ALSO
CONTEMPORARY
DIAGRAM)
HUTTED CAMP

UPPER
NEUADD
RESERVOIR

LOWER
NEUADD
RESERVOIR

TO BRECON
(ROMAN
ROAD)

A 470 (T)

NANT CREW

NANT DDU

TAF FECHAN

CANTREF
RESEVOIR

A 4059

CANTREF FILTERS
COMPLETED 1928
NANT-DDU LODGE

NANT WERN DDU

N

TO PENDERYN

BRIDGE

CUTTING

GARW NANT FAWR

NANT GWINEU

NANT CAR

PONT NANT GWINEU

PONT AR-DAF

PONT-AR-DAF
SIDINGS &
CURTAILED
CIRCA 1897

LLWYN-ON
RESERVOIR

FARMERS' ARMS

ORIGINAL RAILWAY TO CANTREF & BEACONS
WAS ON WEST BANK OF STREAM 1886-'97
CURTAILED AT PONT-AR-DAF CIRCA 1897.
NEW LINE FOR THE EXTENSION OF CANTREF
FILTERS, CIRCA 1931-38, ON THE SITE
OF THE PRESENT ROAD.

NANT ABER NANT

WORKSHOPS
& LOCO SHED

HUTTED
CAMP

SIDINGS ON THE
ORIGINAL LINE
LATER OBLITERATED
BY LLWYN-ON DAM.

TO PENDERYN

NANT BYCHBANT

AFON TAF FAWR

A 470 (T)

VAYNOR
QUARRY

TO PONTSTICILL

TREFECHAN

QUARRY
WITH
SIDING
ROAD BRIDGE 1926
TWO PARTS OF CEMETERY
OVER DEEP VALLEY TRESTLE

CEFN-COED-
Y-CYMMER

A 465 (T)

TO
NEATH

HEADS OF THE VALLEYS
ROAD AND BRIDGE 1966-71

GELLIDEG

TO BATH ROAD

TO
MERTHYR
TYDFIL

## CWM TAF FAWR
### THE VALLEY OF THE BIG TAFF RIVER

## RAILWAYS TO
## BEACONS, CANTREF
## AND LLWYN-ON
## RESERVOIRS

ONE MILE

S.G. RAILWAYS
ROADS
ROADS (SUBMERGED)
HEIGHT OF LAND

ARTHUR CHAMBERS AUG 1973.

The heaviest engineering feature on the private railway was the trestle bridge over the river, where it passes through a rocky gorge immediately north of Cefn; this bridge would be roughly 50ft above the river and some 150ft long. The route then stayed on the west side of the stream, first on a shelf well above the river and then in the bottom of the valley through the site of the later Llwynon Reservoir. As already suggested it may have re-crossed the stream near Nant-Ddu Lodge.

The principal landowners through whose estates the private railway passed on the upper portion of the route to Cantref were Sir William T Lewis (later Baron Merthyr) and Lord Tredegar; the extension proposed to the site of Beacons dam at grid reference SN 988182, higher still up the valley, would have to run through lands of Lord Tredegar. In October 1891, terms for a further six-years passage through Sir William Lewis' lands were being negotiated, apparently amicably; the route was to be securely fenced, with gates at level crossings where considered necessary, free transport of farm needs from Cefn Coed was to be provided, and the land was to be restored afterwards or, at his discretion, the landowner would have the option of buying the railway.

However, by March 1892 disagreement had developed between Sir William and the Corporation and 91 chains (just over a mile) of the existing railway was being lifted where it passed through his land, four farms being involved. It is thought that this would be the section north of the future Llwynon Reservoir and as far as the entry onto the land of

*A view of Cantref Reservoir from the A4059 Brecon to Hirwaun road, 25 May 2004.*     *[Geoffrey Hill]*

*The dam and valve tower of Beacons Reservoir, 25 May 2004.*     *[Geoffrey Hill]*

Lord Tredegar. The Corporation must have been confident that it would eventually be able to secure permission to relay the lifted section as almost concurrently it was completing satisfactory negotiations with Lord Tredegar to take the line through his lands above the west shore of Cantref onwards to Beacons. Indeed, by 22 April 1892 the railway had been extended a short distance on the west shore and a storage area was being established above water level to which plant and materials, then on the bed of Cantref, were to be removed. By January 1893 the surveyors had set out the course throughout from Sir William's upper boundary to the site of Beacons reservoir. Preparation of the formation followed. In April the formation was restored and track relaid over the 91 chains (just over 2,000 yards) through Sir William's land and at midsummer it was reported that two timber viaducts over ravines on the West Shore of Cantref had been built and track laying was complete to Beacons, creating a main line of about 7¼ miles from Cefn Coed. Plans and sections for the extension line from Cantref to the Beacons had been approved by the Board of Trade on 27 April 1893. A fresh Act for the Beacons scheme, enlarged, received assent in August 1894.

The work on the Beacons reservoir was undertaken by direct labour, administered by the Water Department of Cardiff Corporation. A village was built, using as far as possible structures removed from Cantref. In the autumn of 1893, running roads and sidings were laid in at the site and offices, locomotive shed, fitting shop, boiler house, saw mill, carpenters' shops, smithy, wagon shop and stables were erected. Concurrently, excavation for the embankment trench was in hand. The village, shown on the accompanying plan, could accommodate 335 men and accommodation for another 85 was retained at Cantref. The plan is one of the most detailed of its period to survive and is typical of

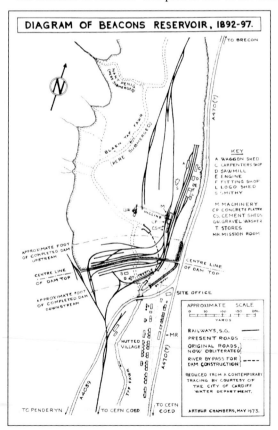

many other reservoir jobs, although naturally laid out to suit the local topography of this bleak site, around 1300-1400ft above sea level. An unusual item of equipment, ordered in February 1894, was 500 yards of "Decauville railway", 15inch gauge (note), with crossings, turntables and wagons, costing £235 6s 0d in all. Its purpose is not known. Crawshay Brothers were to provide the clay on the same terms as for Cantref.

The peak period of activity forming the embankment and putting in its clay core was in 1895-1896, with about 500 men employed on the construction works, clay field, quarry and railway. In February 1896, a record 4,100 tons of clay was dug at the clay field and sent up the railway. The main delays were in bad weather, when labour was diverted from the main work or even laid off altogether. Strangely enough, in September 1895 notice was given that the workmen's train would be discontinued and the Committee, approached by the men, declined to reconsider their decision. This seems an antisocial economy, at a busy period. Presumably the men from Cantref village would have to walk morning and night and those from Cefn Coed would be forced to live at Beacons or contrive lifts on the clay trains. The clay traffic ended round about Christmas 1896 and the work at site was finished off in the spring and summer of 1897. The valves were closed on 17 September and impounding began. The ceremonial inauguration took place on 30 September 1897 by the Chairman, Alderman David Jones JP, as at Cantref, with J A B Williams on record again as the Engineer.    Mr Orton, too, had reprised his role as Resident Engineer and Manager.   Immediately before this ceremony most of the buildings at Beacons were dismantled and many sidings removed. The remaining sidings and the main line back to below Cantref were removed in March – June 1898. Probably track lifting somewhat further down the valley followed during that summer.   Sales of surplus plant had started with that at the clay field around April 1897.   A first sale at Beacons was on 27 July 1897.   During 1897 - 1898 Mr Orton sold various plant and "a final sale of the Cardiff Water Works plant at the Beacon" was announced for 2 September 1898.

## Locomotives

### *Standard gauge*

Recapitulating, work at Cantref was in the hands of William Jones, 11/1885 - 10/1888; John Mackay, 3/1889 - 6/1891; and direct labour under Cardiff Corporation, 7/1891 - 9/1892.   That at Beacons was all by Cardiff Corporation and covered 6/1893 - summer 1897, with opening in September 1897. Mackay took over Jones' plant (which was in formal possession of the Corporation) but did not pay for it; thus it reverted to the Corporation when Mackay withdrew in June 1891.   The first locomotive probably arrived in about April 1886 and was used by Jones; he may have acquired more than one but no evidence of this was found by HDB in his researches.   Industrial Railway Society (IRS) records suggest Jones had two locos here, COUNTESS OF JERSEY and SWANSEA.   In March 1889, Mackay had received another loco, the first addition in his era apparently.   In May 1889 additional plant brought to site by Mackay included four locos (these would embrace the one which he had brought a couple of months or so earlier).   Thus one would expect Mackay to be running one or two ex-Jones locomotives and four of his own.

The following list, compiled by HDB, includes seven standard gauge locos, of which three or four date from the Mackay era, whilst the Corporation obtained one loco second hand in 1891, a new one in 1891 and another new one in 1894. (One three-foot-gauge locomotive was also used by Mackay and is listed separately.)

COUNTESS (or COUNTESS OF JERSEY)   0-6-0 saddle tank   ic 13in x 18in.
    by Hunslet 63 of 1871 - new to Yniscedwyn Iron, Steel & Coal Co Ltd, under a Swansea address in 7/1871. With William Jones on his Rhondda & Swansea Bay Railway contract by c.1883 and later at Cantref with him. The makers record her as later owned by John Mackay as COUNTESS OF JERSEY and subsequently owned by Cardiff Corporation.   Cardiff minutes mention the loco once. They record that COUNTESS (sic) suffered a breakdown c.10/1891 and a bent axle etc were sent away for repairs.   Renamed CWM TAFF by the Corporation, presumably subsequent to this. Later working for J T Firbank on his GNR Neville Hill - Hunslet contract in Leeds by 28/4/1898. Then via Leeds dealer Tom N Brown to S Pearson & Son by 11/1899 still with the name CWM TAFF. This has been independently corroborated by a recollection of CWM TAFF working on building the GWR Badminton main line, a Pearson contract of 1897 - 1903. Then, by coincidence, later with Mackay & Davies, successors to John Mackay, on their GWR/GCR Joint Rly High Wycombe - Princess Risborough contract from 1902 to 1906, apparently named DONALD.   Believed later with C D Phillips, dealer, at his Gloucester yard. No further  trace.

NEPTUNE    0-6-0 saddle tank   ic 11in x 17in.

   by Manning Wardle 67 of 1863 - new to contractors Brassey & Field, Shrewsbury, as
   PERSEVERANCE, doubtless on railway construction, possibly the widening of the Shrewsbury -
   Hereford line.   The Industrial Locomotive Society (ILS) have a note of PERSEVERANCE (not
   identified) disposed of by Cardiff Corporation in 1897 and an old hand may well have remembered
   the loco by this name but she had become NEPTUNE in Mackay ownership at Cantref.   The
   makers' records confirm both Mackay and Cardiff ownership. To dealer Tom N Brown, Leeds, by
   28/4/1898.   Later in life she belonged to Henry Leetham & Sons Ltd, Hungate Flour Mills, York;
   finally to Hadfields (Hope & Caldon Low Quarries) Ltd, the Derbyshire quarry owners after 4/1930.
   She was still named NEPTUNE at their Hope quarry in 1934 - 1936 and carried a Manning plate
   recording rebuilding by the makers in 1910. She still retained an open cab for a while at this
   inhospitable location, but by 8/1934 an ungainly cover had been provided. She was scrapped in
   1939.

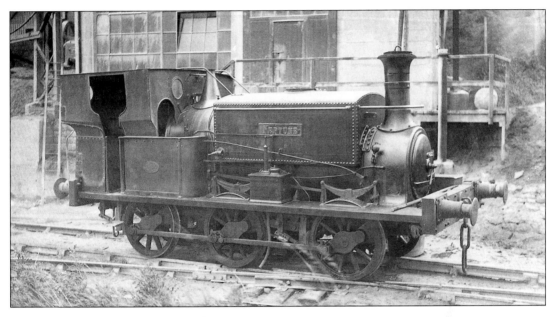

*Manning Wardle 67 of 1863, originally named* PERSEVERANCE, *was owned at Cantref and
Beacons by both John Mackay and the Corporation. At some point she was renamed* NEPTUNE *and is
seen here at Hadfield's Hope Quarry, Derbyshire on 11 August 1934.*        [B D Stoyel, ILS Collection]

SWANSEA

   A loco of this name, at Cantref with Cardiff Corporation, inconveniently broke down c.10/1891,
   concurrently with COUNTESS, and was "sent to the makers in Leeds for repairs". HDB sought to
   identify this engine with SWANSEA  0-6-0 saddle tank ic 12in x 17in. MW 595 of 1876. This loco
   had a complex history, which HDB speculated on as follows: new to contractors Logan &
   Hemingway as N°.6 and then on T A Walker's work at Swansea Harbour c.1879 (job of 1879 -
   1885); recalled on the Manchester Ship Canal contract (1887 - 1894) and then with Price, Wills &
   Reeves building Heysham Harbour, a contract of 1897 - 1904. Could she have left the MSC by
   10/1891 and worked until 1897 for Cardiff (unlikely)?  More likely would be that she was sold by
   Walker from Swansea about 1885 to Jones and worked at Cantref for Jones, Mackay and Cardiff
   until 10/1891, then being resold by Mannings, after repair, to the MSC job and used there until
   completion in 1894, then passing to Price, Wills & Reeves at Heysham. This is credible and would
   enable HDB's old friends to have seen her in the later years of the Ship Canal construction. (Please
   see the notes after this list of locomotives for an alternative identification of SWANSEA).

KAFFIR   0-4-0 saddle tank  oc  8in x 14 in.

    by Manning Wardle 560 of 1875, rebuilt in 1898.  New to contractor John Bayliss of Carlisle as EUSTACE, 26/5/1875. Later with Eckersley & Bayliss and on their Acton to Hounslow contract completed in 1884.  Figures in MW records as Cardiff Corporation's KAFFIR under Merthyr Tydfil, an obvious point of delivery for loco or spares for Beacons.  On 19/11/1897, the sale by the Corporation (from Beacons) of a loco named KAFFIR to Bute Works Supply Co, the Cardiff dealers, was being negotiated but the sale fell through.  The loco was subsequently auctioned on 16-17/12/1897, and was with Leeds dealer Tom N Brown by 4/1898.  Later owners included contractor C J Wills at Sudbury, Middx, c.1910, and the Mitchell Conveyor Co. in the1930s.

CEFN   0-6-0 saddle tank  ic 12in x 18in.

    by Hunslet 256 of 1881 - new to contractors Baker and Firbank, at Lincoln, as DUNSTON; subsequently despatched 7/12/1891 by Hunslet to Cardiff Corporation with name CEFN.  On 7/2/1896 a new steel crank axle was to be supplied and fitted to CEFN by Hunslet for £38 (Corporation minutes).  Offered at the 27/71897 auction; to C D Phillips, the Newport dealer.  She also passed through the hands of Tom N Brown, the Leeds dealer/repairer, c.3/1898.  Then with Pauling and Co. by 4/1899; on their GWR/GCR Jt. contract at Gerrards Cross in 1905 and still with them on their Slimbridge Explosives Depot, Gloucs, contract from c.11/1915; then staying in the same locality at "H M Gloucester Magazine", Slimbridge, (by 7/1917) until moving again to C D Phillips after WW1 (c.1921).  Possibly with Phillips until he gave up his engineering and hiring activities in 1935; a loco fitting this description was included in the closing sale in 4/1935.

*Hunslet 256 of 1881 named* CEFN *was certainly owned by the Corporation and possibly also by both William Jones and John Mackay at Cantref previously. She is seen here in Pauling's ownership working at Denham, Bucks, in the early 1900s.*    *[ILS Collection]*

CANTREFF   0-6-0 saddle tank  ic 12in x 17in.

    by Manning Wardle 1235 of 1891 (note the original spelling for Cantref); - a new loco, ordered by Cardiff Corporation on 9/10/1891, received at Cantref site on Saturday 17/10/1891 and put to work on Monday 19/10/1891.  One can imagine the proud driver allocated to this loco, and his "rope runner", lending a hand to the fitters to get the engine into trim that autumn weekend.  In Beacons'

*Manning Wardle 1235 of 1891 was Cardiff Corporation's* CANTREFF *at Cantref and Beacons but is seen here in later life with Byfield Ironstone Co Ltd, Northants, where she survived until 1962.     [Frank Jones]*

*Llwynon Reservoir, looking south to the dam, on 25 May 2004. The contractor's railway to Cantref and thence to Beacons ran past the reservoir on the far (west) bank.                    [Geoffrey Hill]*

days, 11/1895, new tubes were ordered for this loco and in 10/1896 it was to be sent to Mannings for repairs. The loco was auctioned on 2/9/1898 and was at Newport by 11/1898 (with dealer C D Phillips, perhaps), then that month purchased for £775 and sent per GWR to Westleigh Stone & Lime Co Ltd, Burlescombe, Devon. She passed through Pecketts' hands in 1926 (in part exchange for a new loco) and was sold by them to the Byfield Ironstone Co, Northants, in 6/1929. She enjoyed a very long career there before being scrapped, c.3/1962.

BEACON   0-4-0 saddle tank  oc 10in x 16in.
by Manning Wardle 1259 of 1894 came new to the Corporation, it having been resolved 14/12/1894 that a new engine at £800 be ordered from Manning Wardle of Leeds "and their offer of £40 for the old engine be accepted". BEACON was auctioned on 2/9/1898 and passed to Bute Works Supply Co., Cardiff, thence in 11/1898 to the Marlborough & Grafton Rly. She was later used on service duties at Cirencester works, MSWJR, until at least 1910 and was subsequently in colliery service in the Rhondda Valley. She was scrapped at Blaenclydach Colliery in 7/1928 (according to the late B D Stoyel).

It is interesting to speculate on the identity of the "old engine" sold to Manning Wardle for £40 in 1894. HDB suggested that a locomotive with possible Cwm Taff associations was an 0-4-0 saddle tank  oc 10in x 16in, Manning Wardle 553, new to contractors Scott and Edwards at Holyhead in 8/1875 with the name ANGLESEY. She was recorded by the makers as later owned by John Mackay on his LSWR Weybridge contract in 1887. HDB thought she might have been brought by Mackay to Cantref and thus to Cardiff Corporation ownership in 1891. However, IRS records have this loco later on Mackay's Maidenhead –Twyford widening contract for the GWR, which ran from 1891-1894, so perhaps she never passed to Corporation ownership in 1891. She could not have been SWANSEA, which the records of the IRS identify with Jones, Mackay and Cardiff Corporation as Hunslet 256. In 12/1891 this became CEFN in Corporation ownership (and appearing as such in HDB's list) and for which a new crank axle was ordered in 2/1896, and so clearly was not the engine sold in 1894.

Concerning disposals, it may be noted that in January 1896 contractors Holme and King, building Neuadd reservoir in the next valley for Merthyr Tydfil Corporation, expressed interest in buying surplus plant from Beacons and they were still interested in March that year. Did they in fact secure any locomotives? As previously noted, the first auction at Beacons was on 27 July 1897 (see *Engineer*, 16/7/1897) when two six-coupled locos by Manning Wardle and Hunslet were offered. Another sale on 16-17 December 1897 (see *Contract Journal*, 8/12/1897) offered three six-coupled locos, 11in, 12in and 13in and one 8in four-coupled loco. (The 11in would be PERSEVERANCE, the 13in CWM TAFF and the 8in KAFFIR). In January 1898 Birmingham Corporation, seeking plant for the Elan Valley waterworks project, sought to buy CANTREFF and BEACON but this sale fell through, as Birmingham only offered £500 for the two – Cardiff were looking for £1,250! (Birmingham, in fact, bought new locomotives.) The final sale at Beacons, on 2 September 1898 (see *Engineer*, 26/8/1898), included two locomotives, six wheeled and four wheeled. As we have seen, these would have been CANTREFF and BEACON. In all, eight standard gauge locomotives were involved in these three sales suggesting that some were offered more that once.

### 3ft gauge

DARRELL   0-4-0  saddle tank  oc 7in x12in
by Hudswell Clarke & Rodgers 191 of 1877 - new to Bargoed Coal Co., Fochriw, Glam, as COBB. For sale "close to Darran station" - south of Fochriw on the B & M route - in early 1885 (*Colliery Guardian*, 30/1/1885). This loco worked at the clay field on the Crawshays' Cyfarthfa property referred to earlier. She is assumed to have been here in Mackay's ownership (when clay working for Cantref started). The first minuted record of a loco of this name was on 5/2/1897 in Cardiff Corporation ownership on the Beacons job when it was about to be sold to Crawshay Brothers for £150. She became CYFARTHFA 14 with Crawshays at Cyfarthfa Ironworks. No subsequent trace.

## Chapter 2

# Cardiff's Llwynon Project in Cwm Taf

Plans and sections for the Llwynon dam (at grid reference SO 011113) were prepared for the parliamentary session 1908-09 and an Act of 1909 was secured for the reservoir, providing for roughly double the capacity originally intended. It was decided to employ contractors. The contract was let in November 1910 to Mr Louis P Nott (variously described as of Llanelly and later Bristol) who tendered £201,077 and it allowed six years from January 1911 for completion of the works. These progressed in a business-like way but in 1915, when about half complete, were suspended due to wartime conditions and on the order of HM Treasury. The contract was terminated by mutual agreement in 1919 and Cardiff Corporation resumed work at about that date, using direct labour under Mr Charles H Priestley, their Water Engineer, and Mr H W B Cotterill. The latter had been Resident Engineer since 1910 and now became Resident Engineer and Manager. Mr George Wainfer was "walking ganger" (or site foreman). The valves were partly closed on 23 June 1926 at a ceremony by Alderman W P Francis, JP, Lord Mayor of Cardiff, and impounding of water started. The lake was full by November 1926 but the site was not formally commissioned until May 1927.

Since 1898 the Corporation's railway had ended in a loop short of a level crossing very close to the bridge by which the road from Penderyn crossed the Taf Fawr river in what later became the bed of Llwynon Reservoir. Incidentally, in the dry weather of autumn 1972, the stone bridge carrying this old road over the river was observed exposed to view. Whilst much of the course of the railway continuing north to Beacons Reservoir is clear to view even at the time of writing (the 1970s), parts in the area of the Tredegar Estate are difficult to locate as Lord Tredegar insisted on restoration of the lands and woodlands. Further, even the portion of the line in existence in 1910 had been lying disused for twelve years. Thus Mr Nott's first work in December 1910-January 1911 was to reconstruct the Cefn viaduct on the private railway and to put the route from Cefn Coed railway yard to the site of the new embankment into order. He built an engine shed at Cefn yard and brought in his first locomotive, a crane and other plant. The locomotive ran men up to the site each day; temporary tracks were laid in there, and stripping of soil commenced prior to excavation. Meanwhile, Llwynon House was made fit and taken over by the Resident Engineer and his assistants. Offices and huts were erected on both sides of the Brecon road near Llwynon House. A school and a mission room followed in the spring, with quarters for their staff. Mr Hicken, of the Navvy Mission Society, commenced duty on 9 May and the mission room was opened on 11 July by the Lord Bishop of Llandaff. By this time excavation was down to rock.

On 28 June 1911 there was an official inauguration ceremony at Llwynon by the Lord Mayor. The party traveled by the 10.30am train from Cardiff Queen Street to Merthyr on the Taff Vale Railway. A report says, "Upon arrival at Merthyr the party were conveyed on the Contractor's Railway and in carriages to the site of the Llwynon Reservoir". It may be that Mr Nott's "passenger train" was permitted to run over the LNWR/B&MR Joint line from Merthyr to Cefn Coed on this occasion, but there is a question mark over this as it is not thought that he had anything better than navvy wagons available for travellers. Mr Nott presented a trowel to the Lord Mayor and Mr Priestley presented a mallet. A keystone was laid. The party later drove from Llwynon to Cantref and Beacons.

Sychpant Quarry at Cefn was opened out again that summer but it was planned to bring some Cornish granite from the De Lank quarries, of United Stone Firms Limited, near Bodmin. Other negotiations ensued for imported stone but the main quarrying was at the Corporation's own quarry.

*An interesting view showing a pipeline under construction from Llwynon Reservoir. The Taf Fawr river is at centre and right and the piers of the Cefn Coed viaduct on the B&M and LNW Joint line run across the top of the picture.*          *[H D Bowtell Collection]*

The plan was to develop a clay field on Crawshay Brothers' property and it has been reported to be the same site as that used for clay when Cantref and Beacons were being built. The location was at Pen-yr-Heolgerrig, a district on the slopes west of Merthyr, though the minutes for March - May 1914 on this subject are difficult to follow. Stripping of topsoil commenced on 4 December 1913 and clay was being got out by February 1914.

By May the contractor had built an engine shed at the clay field and laid a tramroad from the clay field to a siding put in on a Cyfarthfa-owned private line connected to the Cwm Pit line, a private railway of the Cyfarthfa enterprise (by this time controlled by Guest, Keen & Nettlefolds). Cwm Pit was south west of Merthyr at grid reference SO 044043. It is not clear whether the tramroad was standard gauge or, alternatively, narrow gauge with resultant transhipment at the siding. From the Cwm Pit line the clay could be hauled to the B&M line (evidently the LNWR/B&MR Joint line) and thence via a reversal to the reservoir site. The motive power which occupied the shed at the clay field has not been identified, but Nott's six-coupled side tank engine SHARPNESS, at one time on the Manchester Ship Canal contract, is recalled working this clay traffic through from the Cwm Pit line, over the joint line and the Corporation's route to the site. The trains were often banked from the quarry junction up to Llwynon. These workings operated from May 1914 until November 1915. Already in October 1914 Mr Nott reported difficulty in executing the contract as a result of a shortage of labour due to the war. He closed the quarry for everything but roadstone on 1 February 1915, and completely on 23 October 1915. Getting clay at the clay field ceased on 3 November 1915. Work at the site was wound up; the puddle trench being covered and sealed and a few men were kept on for maintenance.

Nott had completed the water tunnel beneath the dam and diverted the river clear of the works. He had put the concrete foundations into the trench and made considerable progress with the puddling, as already reported. He had built the new Capel Bethel above the Brecon road at Llwynon to replace the old one at Cwm Taf and it was handed over by the Lord Mayor of Cardiff on 18 June 1914. The main road diversion was completed, from near Llwynon offices to near Abercar, and opened on 10 January 1916. In the autumn of 1914 the Corporation of Cardiff purchased Lord Tredegar's Cwm Taf estate, including the house Nant-Ddu Lodge, just below Cantref.

Litigation appears to have been inseparable from the Cardiff Corporation's relations with its waterworks contractors. The legal fight over the settlement with Mr Nott went on right through the war years 1915-1918 and the Corporation appealed against the outcome of arbitration. The decision of the Law Lords was in favour of the contractor by a majority of four to one.

The costs of the fight were some £25,000, about 80 per cent of which was borne eventually by the Corporation. (This information from *The Reminiscences of Robert Brodie*, 1943.) The first significant post-war minute of Cardiff Corporation is dated 20 January 1919 and concerns "arrangements for settlement following the Contractor's successful appeal to the Lords". Sadly Mr Nott failed to see this outcome. His anxieties over the Cardiff arbitration coincided with the death on 27 April 1916 of his son Pat, a captain in the 6th Gloucestershire Regiment and anxiety over his other two sons (both of whom were later killed, in 1917). Louis Nott died on 4 July 1916. Tom Nott was one of his executors. The other was the aforementioned Robert Brodie, a Scottish civil engineer and staunch friend of the Nott family, who started his professional career on the building of the approach railways to the first Tay Bridge in 1877-1879. It was he who continued the business under the title "Executor of L P Nott" and saw the settlement to a conclusion. Brodie's firm was incorporated 19 January 1922 as Nott, Brodie & Company Limited; it was still active, based in Bristol, in 1973.

The decision to resume work, but now by direct labour under the Engineer, C H Priestley, was taken in February 1919 and about £3,750 was spent in purchasing selected plant from Mr Brodie, as Executor of L P Nott. This purchase was completed by May 1919 and it presumably included the sole locomotive from Mr Nott's stock that passed to the Corporation. This was the TUXFORD, repaired in July 1919 and the first to work under the new regime, soon joined by the second-hand NELSON. Details of these and other locomotives at Llwynon follow.

The years 1919 - 1922 were difficult and inflationary times and preparations were not helped by a strike, mainly by navvies, that continued for many months in the latter part of 1920 and ended on 31 January 1921, only to be followed by the national coal strike in the early months of that year. A new locomotive shed, to house most of the locomotives eventually used, was erected in July 1919 downstream of the dam site and close by the river. A locomotive shed was put up at the quarry in November 1921. The shed at Cefn Coed yard was subsequently used mainly by the "Mail" engine; the old DAN-Y-GRAIG and the three new locomotives of 1920 - 1921 have all been recalled on that duty at various times. The passenger coaches were delivered in May 1920, three old main line four-wheelers. In due course the "Mail" ran through from Cefn Coed each day at 6.30am in summer and about 7.30am in the winter, to Cantref, where new filters were being installed, calling at the quarry to set down masons and at Llwynon to set down and pick up men. It returned at the end of the working day.

Workshops were built near the engine shed at Llwynon and huts for those men who lived on the job were built on the eastern slopes. In Nott's time huts were built on both sides of the Brecon road at Llwynon but most of these were considered sub standard in the post-war years and demolished, the new village being entirely below the road and completed in November 1921. A steam navvy was working in the reservoir bed as early as May 1920 and another was delivered new in January 1921

*Looking east at Llwynon. The lack of activity and the date (26 April 1916) tell us we are in the interregnum between Louis Nott giving up the contract and the Corporation restarting work after the war in 1919.* [Harold D Bowtell Collection]

*From the same viewpoint on 28 February 1922 showing work progressing with the puddle clay core of the dam. Nott's workmen's housing has disappeared and both Hudswell Clarke locomotives can be observed at work.* [Harold D Bowtell Collection]

and soon put to work on the bed. Just before Christmas 1921, the severely inclement weather caused the Water Committee to replace the open Ford car used by their Water Engineer by a closed car. This was delivered on 2 March 1922; an Austin 20 four-seater coupe, costing £850. It was the Austin 20hp and smaller Austin 12hp cars of the 1920s, which earned their makers the right to use the slogan "As dependable as an Austin". The purchase was no doubt an acknowledgement that Mr Priestley was 67 years of age at this time. Also in December 1921 arrangements were made to run a school train from Llwynon to Cefn yard in the morning and back in the afternoon on schooldays, parents signing indemnities. Then in February 1922 a navvy missioner took up residence at Llwynon, coming from Beaufort where the Blaen-y-Cwm reservoir works had recently been completed.

In addition to stone from the Corporation's quarry, Forest of Dean stone was brought in to build the valve shaft starting in July 1921 and in early 1922 the railway was extended into the reservoir bottom, to deliver stone for pitching the bank. It is assumed that the bed of the lake had become so much deeper by this time that the old line up the valley floor had disappeared.

Another most significant railway extension took place in 1922 in connection with the new filters and filter house to be built at Cantref, just north of Nant-Ddu Lodge and short of the dam, on the floor of the valley. Stone, cement and machinery had to go to this site. The route through the bed of Llwynon was not followed, a diversion being made, climbing steeply on the western slope of the valley to reach the level eventually attained by the dam and the road that now crosses it. The new line then followed the course subsequently adopted for the west side road, thus keeping above the future water level. North of the new lake the course of the old Beacons line was followed, the use of this route yet again being negotiated with Lord Merthyr. Part of this line must have been laid and lifted three times in its history.

Puddling at the dam was resumed in July 1921, after an interval of nearly six years. Cheaper clay had been found near Neath and was got out by a local contractor, Stephens and Company, but deliveries were irregular. Some clay was brought from Pengam, in both cases by rail throughout. In the month ending 17 July 1922, 185 trucks of clay from Neath and Pengam were placed in the wall and the building up of the earth bank and putting of puddle into the trench continued apace. In the month to 15 October 1923, 176 wagons of clay from Neath and Pengam were put in and 486 contractor's 4½ yard wagon loads of material was deposited in the bank itself, which now approached top level.

Just a year later plant was becoming surplus and an auction was arranged to sell the two steam navvies and three locomotives, amongst other items. Most of the Cantref extension line was lifted in April 1926 and work at the dam was in its final stages. Mr Priestley, the Engineer, retired in April 1926 after 31 years service, aged 72 years. It is interesting to note that in February 1919 the Waterworks Committee, resolving to complete the project with direct labour, had agreed to appoint James Watson, the notable engineer who designed and built much of Bradford's waterworks in the Nidd Valley of Yorkshire, as advisory engineer but his death occurred before this could take effect. After the inauguration of Llwynon Reservoir and Cantref filters on 23 June 1926, work at the quarry was soon ended. Sales of plant at Llwynon took place at intervals for another two years. Various locomotives departed in 1927, and the village and workshops at the site were cleared in May 1928. Lifting of the railway track from Cantref filters had begun in early April 1926 and was complete back through Lord Merthyr's land to the Penderyn road by the end of that month. Probably by early 1928, the line thence to Cefn Coed had been lifted, after a spasmodic life of over forty years. The valley relapsed into peace, not often broken since, except by the noise of traffic, which now grinds or speeds over the road to Brecon. [IRS records state that the railway was sold to T W Ward Ltd for dismantling in 1930. By implication Wards may have used DAN-Y-GRAIG on track lifting trains here.]

*Looking west across the dam with three locomotives at work on 14 July 1922. The line to Cefn Coed comes in at top left and continues top right towards Cantref where new filters were being installed at this time.* *[Harold D Bowtell Collection}*

### The locomotives (all standard gauge) on the Llwynon project

Louis Nott brought at least six locomotives to Llwynon. All seem to have worked previously on his Cammell Laird Dry Dock contract at Birkenhead, Cheshire, which was completed in 1909. After the suspension of work at Llwynon in November 1915, at least three of the locomotives, CHEPSTOW, SHARPNESS and TRANMERE are thought to have been requisitioned by the Ministry of Munitions (MoM) but this is not confirmed

CHEPSTOW    0-6-0 saddle tank   ic 12in x 17in.
> by Manning Wardle 738 of 1881 – new to contractor T A Walker at Swansea, 11/4/1881. Then at his Manchester Ship Canal contract, 1887 - 1890, later coming to Nott at his Llanelli North Dock contract, which ran from 3/1898 to 12/1903. At his Birkenhead contract for the Cammell Laird Dry Dock until c.1909, before coming to Cwm Taf. After suspension of work, to MoM? Later with contractors Muirhead, MacDonald, Wilson & Co Ltd at their Fulham depot, London; used as a hire loco and on their Ilford housing contract for the City of London Corporation 1920 - 1922. At Muirhead's Barkingside, Essex, plant depot from c.1923 to c.1928. No further trace.

NORMAN    0-6-0 saddle tank   ic 12in x 18in.
> by Hunslet 454 of 1888 - originally with T A Walker, on his MSC contract as RUSHOLME; then to H M Nowell, contractor, as NORMAN; to Thomas Oliver's contracts in North London, 1902.  To Nott by 5/1903, on his Princes Risborough - Grendon Underwood contract for the GW & GC Railways Joint Committee until c.1906. Used at Cammell Laird Dry Dock contract until c.1909 before coming to Cwm Taf (here by 5/1912). From Llwynon to William F Blay's Air Ministry contract at Eastleigh aerodrome, Hants, by 18/9/1918, then to MoM possibly at the same site. No trace after 9/1921.

*Sharp Stewart 3472 of 1888 as* TATTON *working on the Manchester Ship Canal construction for her first owner T A Walker. She was later renamed* SHARPNESS *by Louis Nott and worked for him at Llwynon.*                                                                    *[E R Gray Collection]*

*Manning Wardle 1518 of 1901 was named* LIVERPOOL *with Louis Nott at Llwynon. Seen here later in the ownership of Sir Robert McAlpine & Sons Ltd as Nº35 on the Watling Street, Dartford to Strood, contract about 1923.*                                                                    *[H D Bowtell Collection]*

**SHARPNESS**   0-6-0 side tank   ic 13in x 20in.

by Sharp Stewart 3472 of 1888 - originally T A Walker's TATTON on his MSC contract; finding her way to Sir John Jackson (on the continuing MSC job?); then to Nott, probably used by him on his Sharpness Dock Extension contract of 1895 in Gloucs and thus acquiring the name. At Cammell Laird Dry Dock contract until c.1909 as SHARPNESS, before moving to Cwm Taf. Her "main line" run to and from Cyfarthfa clay pit has been recalled. After suspension of work, to MoM? Later with Muirhead, MacDonald, Wilson & Co Ltd, Fulham; used on their Ilford housing contract for the City of London Corpn., 1920 - 1922. She cost Muirhead's £1,804 but she only fetched £87 15s when sold at the end of the job. Nott, Brodie acquired her (their people knew her well!) and they used her on the Avonmouth Portway road contract, from 1922 to 1924, after which time there are no further sightings.

**TUXFORD**   0-6-0 saddle tank   oc 13in x 20in.

by Hunslet 579 of 1893 - originally with S. Pearson & Son (on their Lancs, Derbys & East Coast, Port Talbot and GWR Badminton cut-off contracts) but came to Nott, who used her on the Cammell Laird job and subsequently here at Cwm Taf.  This was the only one of Nott's locos still present here in the later Cardiff Corporation era.

**LIVERPOOL**   0-4-0 saddle tank   oc 12in x 18in.

by Manning Wardle 1518 of 1901 - new to Nott at Liverpool on Canada Branch Dock N°.2 contract until c.1903. Subsequently to Nott's Princes Risborough contract until c.1906, then probably at the Cammell Laird job before coming to Cwm Taf. She passed to Sir Robert McAlpine & Sons Ltd on 6/11/1917, working on his British Celanese factory contract, Spondon, Derbys, initially, and later on other jobs.

*Kitson 1786 of 1871, named* NELSON, *was already a veteran when photographed at Cefn Coed exchange sidings. The station hotel forms a backdrop.*                    *[H D Bowtell Collection]*

**TRANMERE**  0-6-0 saddle tank  ic 13in x 20in.

　　by Hudswell Clarke 654 of 1903 - delivered new to Nott at Calvert Station, GCR, (for the Princes Risborough contract) but presumably (from the name) intended for, and believed worked on, Nott's Cammell Laird job. Brought subsequently to Cwm Taf.  She evidently left Cwm Taf in wartime, used on an ordnance factory project or on loan to such a factory (Hudswell's records associate her with the contractor T Docwra & Son in 1916); then with Executor of L P Nott/Nott, Brodie, c.1918 - 1922, building Blaen-y-Cwm Reservoir, Beaufort, for the Ebbw Vale Steel, Iron and Coal Co Ltd and from 1922 the Avonmouth Portway road, Gloucs. During 1928 - 1930 Nott, Brodie hired her to Edmund Nuttall for his Bartley Reservoir job, Worcs, after Nuttall's shed had been destroyed by fire and his locos damaged beyond repair. She appears to have passed to A R Adams, the Newport dealer, after 1932. No subsequent trace.

Cardiff Corporation, in the period 1919 - 1927, seem to have had three second-hand locomotives on the Cwm Taf job and also three new ones acquired for the purpose:

**TUXFORD**  0-6-0 saddle tank  ic 13in x 18in.

　　by Hunslet 579 of 1893 - taken over from the Executor of L P Nott but in a poor condition.  Repairs to TUXFORD were mentioned in reports of 7/1919 and again 9/1919.  (First spares for the loco in Cardiff ownership were ordered 31/5/1919.)  Before long she was mounted on blocks providing steam for a pump at Llwynon.  In 6/1920 it was proposed to advertise TUXFORD for sale in *Machinery Market*. No further trace.

**NELSON**  0-6-0 saddle tank ic 13in x 20in.

　　by Kitson 1786 of 1871  - recorded as new to Thomas Nelson & Co, Carlisle-based contractors, who did much work in North East England and who probably used her on railway building for the NER. (Teeside has been mentioned, so she may have been used on the Stockton-Castle Eden line contract in 1876 - 1880); disposed of c.1880 (or 1885?) to the Woodland Colliery Co Ltd, Crake Scar Colliery, Lynesack, near West Auckland, which opened about 1880 and closed in 1921. She probably passed to the well-known dealer J F Wake around 1919.  The Corporation bought her at Wake's Darlington yard and Mr Harry Hicken brought her from there in 9/1919.  She carried a J F Wake plate whilst at Llwynon.   A minute of 20/10/1919 notes that NELSON was running in place of TUXFORD, conveying permanent way materials and platelayers.  By 1/1921 the fitters' gang were at work on NELSON. She did some shunting and was photographed more than once working at Cefn Coed but soon took up her stance on blocks for stationary pump duties. No further trace.

**DAN-Y-GRAIG**  0-6-0 saddle tank  ic 13in x 18in.

　　by Manning Wardle 835 of 1882 - new (unnamed) to contractors Lucas and Aird at Hull, probably building the Hull & Barnsley Railway or Alexandra Dock; later with J Aird & Co, and then S Pearson & Son as HERCULES building the GWR Badminton cut-off. She passed briefly through the hands of P Baker, the Cardiff engineer and dealer, c.1905, and was with Topham, Jones & Railton, contractors, on their King's Dock, Swansea, job as DAN-Y-GRAIG. With TJR at Poole Harbour and Oxfordshire Ironstone as well as a period on hire.  She was brought by Mr Hicken from Topham's Crymlyn Burrows yard, Swansea, to Cwm Taf; arrival reported 7/1920.  Later she passed c.2/1930 to T W Ward Ltd. at their Briton Ferry, Glam, shipbreaking yard and may have shunted there as she was not scrapped until about 1936.

**LLWYN-ON**  0-6-0 saddle tank  ic 13in x 20in. (note spelling of name)

　　by Hudswell Clarke 1429 of 1920 - came new to the Corporation; ex makers 17/12/1920, delivery reported by 14/1/1921, but evidently she suffered teething troubles and was put in order by the makers' men during the following month.  Sold 30/9/1927 to T W Ward Ltd., dealers, Sheffield (their Brightside reference N°.37745); to Lever Bros Ltd, Port Sunlight, Cheshire. To contractor Sir Lindsay Parkinson & Co Ltd, as '46'; used on their N°.3 Fish Dock contract at Grimsby, Lincs, which finished in 1935, then to their ROF Chorley contract, Lancs, 1937-1939. By 5/1940 with Brynn Hall Colliery Co. Ltd., near Wigan, Lancs, as JAMES - a name retained for a later existence with British Sugar Corporation: at Ipswich factory, Suffolk from c.5/1946, at King's Lynn factory, Norfolk by 8/1952 and at Felsted factory, Essex from c.1953. She was seen derelict at the latter site in 1957 and subsequently scrapped.

*Hudswell Clarke 1466 of 1921,* CWM TAFF, *at the interchange sidings at Cefn Coed station with a workmen's 'paddy' train The station hotel is in the background and the gate, extreme right, probably gave access to the station.* [Harold D Bowtell Collection]

*Hudswell Clarke 1429 of 1920, formerly* LLWYN-ON, *seen in the later ownership of the British Sugar Corporation at King's Lynn, Norfolk, where she carried the name* JAMES. [Peter Michie]

Manning Wardle 2015 of 1921, ABERNANT, *was one of three locomotives bought new by the Corporation for Llwynon and is seen here at Cefn Coed.* [Harold D Bowtell Collection]

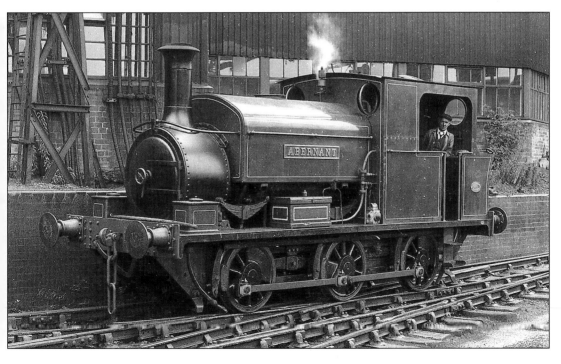

*A very pleasing view of* ABERNANT *in later life at the Austin Motor Co Ltd, Longbridge, Birmingham, on 19 July 1950.* [K J Cooper; Peter Michie Collection]

CWM TAFF   0-6-0 saddle tank   ic 13in x 20in. (note spelling of name)
by Hudswell Clarke 1466 of 1921 - ordered 16/9/1921 for £3,200 and delivered new, leaving the makers on 29/9/1921 for Cefn Coed.  Sold 30/9/1927 to T W Ward, Sheffield (37744); may later have worked briefly for Sheffield Corporation on Ewden Valley waterworks (see *Manchester and the Peak*); to Perry & Co (Bow) Ltd, Bromborough Dry Dock (Lever Bros Ltd) contract, Cheshire, which ended in 1929. To Sir Lindsay Parkinson, as N°.314, by c.1932; then, as with HC1429, to his Grimsby and Chorley contracts and sold to Brynn Hall Colliery Co Ltd, Lancs, by 5/1940, their MARGARET; finally to Settle Limes Ltd, Horton-in Ribblesdale after 1/1946.

ABERNANT   0-6-0 saddle tank   ic 13in x 20in.
by Manning Wardle 2015 of 1921 - ordered the same day as the Hudswell CWM TAFF and at the same price - delivered new: stated to be the last new loco to arrive and the only one with the steam brake.  Driven by Barney McNally. Sold 30/9/1927 to T W Ward, Sheffield, (37743) and thence to the Austin Motor Co Ltd, at Longbridge, near Birmingham, 17/12/1927, where active from 1928 to c.1963. Sold to metal merchant J Cashmore, of Great Bridge, Birmingham, 20/11/1963, and installed in a children's playground in Newdigate Street, Birmingham - just over the wall from the electrified lines of British Railways near Vauxhall (Birmingham) Station, 19/2/1964; this playground seems later to have became known as the Ashtead Walk playground, Duddeston.  Thereafter the loco has had many wanderings in preservation but has yet to be restored: she moved to the Standard Gauge Steam Trust, Birmingham Railway Museum, Tyseley, West Midlands, 13/7/1989; then to Peter Elms, at North Woolwich Station museum site, London; to Peak Rail at Rowsley South, Derbys, in 6/2002; and to the Nottingham Transport Heritage Centre, Ruddington, Notts, in 2003.

The Corporation of Cardiff offered three 13in 0-6-0 locomotives for sale in 1925, also one for sale as scrap (*Machinery Market*, 2/1/1925). On 7/9/1927 (*Contract Journal*) they offered plant including locos for sale at Llwynon Reservoir. Again in the *Contract Journal*, 1/2/1928 two 0-6-0 locomotives were offered (one of these would be DAN-Y-GRAIG).  Maybe the three locomotives offered were the modern ones, which eventually sold in 1927, with either TUXFORD or NELSON designated as scrap. This would leave the other two for disposal in 1928. DAN-Y-GRAIG and the three new locomotives were all recalled by visitors to Cantref filters during the progress of works there.

*A fine line-up at Llwynon in Cardiff Corporation days. Left to right are* ABERNANT, DAN-Y-GRAIG, NELSON, CWM TAFF *and* LLWYN-ON.  *Only* TUXFORD *is missing, possibly on stationary boiler duties. 14 March 1923.*                                                   *[Harold D Bowtell collection]*

# Other Cardiff projects nearer the city

## *Ely Waterworks*

Cardiff Waterworks Company was formed in 1850 and provided a piped water supply to the city from wells at Ely, some three miles to the west, from 1852. Cardiff Corporation bought the water undertaking from the private company in 1879. Ely Waterworks was being extended in 1881 by the contractors Jones & Jepson of Neath, one of whose principals was William Jones, later to work for the Corporation at Cantref Reservoir (1886 - 1888). At the end of the job an auction was announced in the *Western Mail*, 31/12/1881, of surplus plant including temporary rails. A subsequent sale at the contractors yard in Neath on 14/3/1882 offered all their contractors' plant including a "four wheel locomotive, 10 inch cylinders, by Hughes of Loughborough" plus 80 earth wagons and four ballast wagons. No further information is available although it must be a possibility that the locomotive was used at Ely.

The Ely wells remained in regular use for household supply until 1926. In recent times they have been a source of water for the Aberthaw Power Station.

## *Llanishen Reservoirs*

In 1882, before the burgeoning industry and population of Cardiff led the Corporation to look to the Brecon Beacons for its water needs, the Corporation embarked on the construction of reservoirs at Llanishen, nowadays a northern suburb of the city. The larger 317 million gallon reservoir is located at grid reference ST 188818 a short distance to the east of the Rhymney Railway main line and to the south of Llanishen station. The contractor was the well-known John Mackay, who later was engaged by Cardiff at Cantref Reservoir (1889-1891); he doubtless used a railway in the construction works but no details of this have survived. It would certainly have made connection with the Rhymney line.

Almost as soon as the works were completed the Corporation must have decided to enlarge the installation. A contract for this work was awarded to Hill Brothers, probably in 1884. They were unable to carry on from July of the same year, having lost £2,000 on a sewerage contract at High Wycombe, Bucks, and the work was taken over by T A Walker, who was coming towards the end of the herculean task of building the Severn Tunnel for the GWR. Walker was involved at Llanishen from September 1884-1886. The smaller (northernmost) reservoir of 80 million gallons at grid reference ST 189821 has in modern times become known as Lisvane Reservoir. It is not clear at the present if the Hill Brothers/T A Walker project referred to earlier involved this reservoir or an extension of the larger reservoir.

### Locomotives

No locomotives have been identified at Llanishen under Mackay or Hill Brothers ownership but at least three are known to have been used by Walker:

#### *Standard gauge*

ROMILLY  0-6-0 saddle tank   ic 12in x 18in
> by Hunslet 357 of 1885 - new to T A Walker at Llanishen 17/3/1885 (believed named after Lord Romilly, a local landowner), and afterwards to Walker's celebrated Manchester Ship Canal contract of 1887 - 1890. To the Manchester Ship Canal Railway Dept's fleet in 1894 as N°. 2; sold (for scrap?) in 1932/1933.

*Hunslet 357,* ROMILLY, *was new to T A Walker's Llanishen reservoir contract in 1885, later passing to a long association with the Manchester Ship Canal contract and the canal company's own fleet. Seen here in beautiful condition at the MSC's Mode Wheel shed, still carrying her name on the toolbox.*

*[Peter Michie Collection]*

RHYMNEY  0-4-0 saddle tank  oc 12in x 18in
> by Hunslet 380 of 1886 - new to Walker here, 1/2/1886, and then to his Manchester contract, 1887 to 1890. Later with the MSC Railway Dept's fleet – spares delivered to there as late as 9/1899. Sold by MSC 'pre1914' and with the Glamorganshire Canal Co, Cardiff, then probably with the Taff Rhondda Navigation Steam Coal Co Ltd at Nantgarw Colliery from c.1912. Later still with the Provincial Coal Co at Merthyr Tydfil in the 1922-1928 period.

DOUGLAS  0-4-0 saddle tank  oc 13in x 18in
> by Hunslet 381 of 1886 - new to Walker here, 10/9/1886, and then to the Manchester contract. Later to the MSC Railway Dept's fleet as N°.5 and mainly used as an inspection loco. (A recess was added at the back of the cab and a seat installed for Mr W Fox, the MSC's Mechanical Engineer). The loco was sold at an unknown date.

### 2ft gauge

Many years after its construction, in 1929-1930, the Corporation dredged the reservoir using direct labour. They used a 2ft gauge railway and a locomotive:

- 0-4-0 saddle tank  oc 6in x 9in  'Wren' class
> by Kerr Stuart 4161 of 1921, which had been used on the Wenallt Reservoir construction (which see). She came to Llanishen c.1929 and was sold to the Cardiff dealer Frank Munn in March 1930; by August 1932 she was at the Stoneycombe Lime & Stone Co Ltd's quarry beside the GWR's Dainton bank near Newton Abbot, Devon, where she saw many years of service.

# Rhiwbina Waterworks

The works (at grid reference ST 149825?) was constructed by John Mackay, beginning in 1888. It was later served by a siding on the north side of the Cardiff Railway line (opened 1902) between Rhiwbina and Whitchurch stations. No information is available on the use of railways by the contractor (or subsequently by the Corporation) but this is a possibility.

# Heath Filter Beds

Anticipating the completion of Beacons Reservoir in 1897, the Corporation awarded a contract to Thomas D Ridley of Cardiff and Middlesbrough for an enlargement of the facilities at Heath Filter Beds in the northern suburbs of the city (grid reference ST 181796). A service reservoir and three filter beds were already in place here. Ridleys were to install a further three beds at a contract price of £10,114 17s 6d. They commenced putting plant on the ground on 5/4/1897 and work was completed by 1/3/1898. A siding had been put in at the site from the adjoining Rhymney Railway and virtually all materials were brought in by rail. Surplus spoil was taken to Cardiff Docks for use in a new embankment and all sand and gravel were brought by sailing ships and steamers from Bideford, Devon, to quayside in Cardiff. A further contract saw Ridleys providing two more filter beds and a second service reservoir at the site by the end of 1898. A narrow gauge Decauville portable railway was installed for removing and replacing the filter bed sand and gravel. No further details of the railway layouts or the possible use of locomotives on either gauge are known.

# Wenallt Reservoir

A relatively small job that was a long time in the building, this was a service reservoir (at grid reference ST 154825) to hold 15 million gallons of treated water. It occupies an upland site on the northwestern outskirts of Cardiff, with the attractive woodlands, Coed-y-Wenallt, rising to the north. The design involved concrete walls around the reservoir, which has since been roofed over.

The Corporation started the construction using direct labour in June 1920. In October/November they were laying a railway from the reservoir grounds to the bottom of the field. A small locomotive was at work by November that year. On 23/5/1921 "N°.2 loco" was reported to have been delivered to this site and to be at work. In the latter part of 1922 a siding was put in at Whitchurch station on the Cardiff Railway line (which now ends at Coryton, as a purely suburban branch) and an aerial ropeway was built from here to the site, about one mile. Direct labour work was suspended in March 1924. In October 1924, a contract for construction was placed with Hybart, Broadhead & Company, and they soon started work, using the Corporation's ropeway, mainly it is thought to bring in cement for the concrete walls. They evidently also used the Corporation's railway on site. Snapshots of the site dated 3/3/1926 show a small steam locomotive, with "wing" side tanks and a cab, running probably on 2ft gauge tracks. On 31/3/1926 the contract was terminated. This was probably because subsidence had occurred. The Corporation assumed responsibility for construction once more. Borings were made by specialists, the Francois Cementation Company, who undertook remedial work in 1926 - 1927. Eventually, Wenallt reservoir was filled, half in November 1927 and half in February 1928. The ropeway was dismantled in October 1927 and doubtless the railway too. Sale of the plant took place between 10/1927 and 10/1928.

## Locomotives

### *2ft gauge*

Two 0-4-0 saddle tank oc locomotives by Kerr Stuart, named ROBIN and WREN, are believed to have worked here in the late 1920s.

- 0-4-0 saddle tank   oc 6in x 9in
  by Kerr Stuart 3114 of 1918, of the 'Wren' class, came here second hand from the Ministry of Munitions, Driffield, Yorks (ER), by 11/1920. HDB has noted that this locomotive possibly left Wenallt, c.1926 and may have been used by Lehane, Mackenzie & Shand, contractors, on their Brownhill Reservoir job at Holmbridge, West Yorks, for Batley Corporation, which ran from 1924 - 1932. However, there seems to be no direct evidence that she was at Brownhill. It is known that Lehanes used her on their Vyrnwy pipeline contract in Cheshire, c.1930; an entry in W G Bagnall's spares ledgers dated 4/9/1930 reveals that parts for the locomotive were to be delivered to Delamere, Northwich, Cheshire. (This would have been after the closure of Kerr Stuart's works. Bagnall 2080 of 1918, a 6 x 9in 0-4-0ST, also worked on this latter job for Lehanes and had been purchased by them from Sir Robert McAlpine in late 1929). So the exact sequence of this engine's early work for Lehanes is uncertain. She was definitely recorded (and photographed) later on Lehanes' contract at Fernilee Reservoir for Stockport Corporation, 1932 - 1937, and eventually passed to William Twigg, the Matlock dealer, c.1944, and later still into preservation.

- 0-4-0 saddle tank   oc 6in x 9in
  by Kerr Stuart 4161 of 1921, another 'Wren', was new to the Corporation at Whitchurch, presumably for this project, c.4/1921. She moved to the Corporation's Llanishen Reservoir (which see) on dredging work, c.1929.

Clearly these locomotives would not answer to the description of the engine in the photograph mentioned earlier.


# *Llandegfedd Reservoir*

This large 5,390 million gallon reservoir was developed by the Corporation and opened in two stages in the spring of 1964 and 1965. It is situated in the valley of the Sor Brook three miles to the east of Pontypool, Monmouthshire, at grid reference SO 330995, very close to the Glascoed ordnance factory. The reservoir is filled mainly by pumping water from the River Usk by means of an intake at Prioress Mill, Rhadyr, near Usk. The dam is an earth embankment with a rolled clay core. Water is filtered at the Sluvad treatment works before passing down a gravity aqueduct to Cardiff.

In 1965 the planned allocation of the waters was to be:

| | |
|---|---|
| *Cardiff Corporation* | *9 million gallons per day* |
| *Newport & South Monmouthshire Water Board* | *5 million gallons per day* |
| *Abertillery & District Water Board* | *3 million gallons per day* |
| *Pontypool & District Water Co.* | *3 million gallons per day* |

In addition 1,825 million gallons per year were to be made available to Richard Thomas & Baldwin's Spencer Steel Works at Llanwern, Monmouthshire, which opened in September 1961.

The name of the main contractor involved on this project is not at present known and no information exists on the use of railways at the site.

*Kerr Stuart 3114 of 1918 was used on the construction of Wenallt service reservoir for the Corporation in the 1920s. She is seen later when working for Lehane, Mackenzie & Shand at Fernilee reservoir, Derbyshire about 1935. Happily she survived to be preserved.* [R W Miller Collection]

*Kerr Stuart 4161 of 1921 was bought new by the Corporation for the Wenallt job, but photographed at Stoneycombe Lime & Stone Co's quarry in Devon years later. Note the 'Frank Munn, Cardiff' dealers' plate on the upper cab side.* [ILS Collection]

# Chapter 3

# The Valley of the Taf Fechan

### Railways serving the Neuadd & Taf Fechan Reservoirs of Merthyr Tydfil Corporation and the Taf Fechan Water Supply Board

A few miles east of the main Taff valley (Cwm Taf), containing the Taf Fawr (or Great Taff) river, lies the valley of the Taf Fechan (or Little Taff). This stream also originates on the southern slopes of the Beacons and joins with the Taf Fawr between Cefn Coed and Merthyr Tydfil to form the river Taff - well known to railway enthusiasts thanks to the proximity of the Taff Vale Railway for all the twenty-four miles from Merthyr Tydfil to Cardiff.

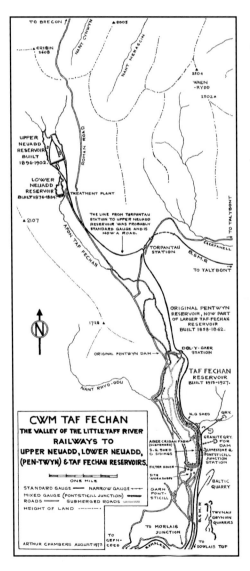

## Neuadd Reservoirs

Bleak Torpantau station on the Brecon and Merthyr Railway was 1,310ft above sea level. Merthyr Tydfil Corporation bought land and built a private branch line, 1½ miles long, westward from the B&MR at Torpantau in order to carry materials for a small reservoir, of 74 million gallons capacity, called Lower Neuadd (at grid reference SO 030180). The relevant Act was of 1876. The bank is of earth and would involve importing puddle clay. It was completed in 1884 but the dates 1882-1888 have been associated with the work here of the contractor, William Jones of Neath. Top water level is at 1,413ft above ordnance datum (o.d.). The line to Lower Neuadd was an early example of a purpose-built railway for dam building. The actual work on site would be on a modest scale, probably handled by steam cranes and winches, horses and manpower. It would be interesting to know whether the branch was worked by horses, by a private locomotive or by a loco of the B&MR. The project is recalled by the name of "The Zulu", derived from the coincidence of the Zulu war (1879 - 1880) with the early days of its construction.

An extension of almost a mile, taking off from the original line, was added by the Corporation in order to reach the site of Upper Neuadd reservoir dam (at grid reference SO 030188), built under an Act of 1895 during the years 1896 - 1902. It was a larger reservoir, of 340 million gallons capacity, set in a wild valley; its top water level of 1,506ft puts it in the small and select class of British man-made lakes above 1,500ft. This time the dam, 75ft high, was built in masonry, set in concrete, the body being of cyclopean rubble, namely massive rough-hewn stones, and the exterior of dressed

*The grand but inhospitable setting of Upper Neuadd reservoir at over 1,500 ft. Taf Fechan reservoir is glimpsed in the centre distance; Craig Fan-Ddu is at right.* [Harold D Bowtell Collection]

limestone. The dam was designed by Mr George F Deacon, Consulting Engineer of Westminster, and the official opening was on 10 July 1902.

Unusual arrangements were made for the work at Upper Neuadd. A contract let to Holme and King, of Liverpool, embraced the cutting away of the rock to level in the central portion of the dam site, the cutting and timbering of the trenches east and west of the rock river bed, the quarrying near Dowlais of the large limestone and mortar, provision of locomotive engines, machinery and plant, including gantries along the dam, the execution of temporary works, the conveyance from Torpantau station along the Council's temporary railway of all the stone and other materials and their delivery as required on site. However, the Corporation, by direct labour supervised by Mr Thomas F Harvey, surveyor to the Corporation and here acting as Resident Engineer, undertook to deposit and ram the concrete in the foundations and to build the dam. The quarry referred to was subsequently described as being between Pant and Pontsticill and the B&MR hauled about 100,000 tons of stone to Torpantau at ten pence per ton. (Mr Harvey had an extraordinary career in water supply in the area. He joined Merthyr's Water Department in 1885 and was still in harness in the town as Engineer to the Taf Fechan Water Board at the time of official opening of the Pontsticill Reservoir in 1927.)

The formation of the route from Torpantau to Lower Neuadd and Upper Neuadd is suitable for standard gauge and references in the writings of Mr Harvey support its being standard gauge. Photographs of Upper Neuadd works in progress show the construction lines depicted on our map and the wagons in these pictures appear to be standard gauge ones. A low roofed four-wheel saloon carriage also appears at the site. Under the terms of the contract, Holme and King would be expected to provide locomotives. However, only one standard gauge locomotive has, to date, been identified with Neuadd, namely:

37

**BEATRICE   0-4-0 saddle tank   oc 10in x 16in**
by Manning Wardle 768 of 1881. This was new as LEOPARD to Thomas Monk, a contractor doing river improvements for the River Witham Commissioners, Boston, Lincs. Holme & King acquired her at a date unknown. She was presumably at Upper Neuadd from c.1896 and passed in 1902 to Henllys Vale Anthracite Co. Ltd. Upper Cwmtwrch, Carms.

The *Contract Journal*, 4/6/1902 announced that J Forrester (an auctioneer?) was to sell, 18/6/1902, for Holme & King and Merthyr Tydfil UDC re Merthyr Tydfil Waterworks, Upper Neuadd Reservoir, plant including a locomotive. This would seem to be the standard gauge BEATRICE. Three interesting photographs have come to light in circumstances that imply association with Upper Neuadd. One shows the contractor's site office and the beautiful turnout of his (or his agent's) personal transport. The others show Holme & King's well-known 3ft gauge engine XIT (see below and next page). The background is not easily related to Neuadd but maybe shows the trench construction in the valley to which the contract refers; in the close-up photograph, complete with dog, workmen, bowler-hatted gaffer and (probably) gaffer's son, the track beneath XIT may well be mixed gauge.

## 3ft gauge

**XIT 0-4-0 saddle tank   oc  8in x 14in**
by Manning Wardle 475 of 1874. This was new to Rosedale & Ferryhill Iron Co Ltd, Rosedale Abbey Ironstone Mines, N. Yorks, as ROSEDALE; later with S Pearson & Son, at their Southport drainage works contract from c.1879 and Blackwall Tunnel job of 1891-97, before passing to Holme & King about 1898. The loco enjoyed a much-traveled career with H & K before returning to South Wales on William Underwood's Penderyn Reservoir contract (Ch. 5; see that chapter for her history subsequent to Upper Neuadd).  HDB in his *Lesser Railways of the Yorkshire Dales* gives the origin of the name as that of a favourite servant, somewhat short in stature, of the young King Edward VI (born 1537, died 1553).

*Holme & King's site office, believed to be at Upper Neuadd, about 1900*          *[H D Bowtell collection]*

38

*The much-traveled 3 ft gauge engine* XIT *(Manning Wardle 475 of 1873) is believed to be shown here at the Upper Neuadd reservoir construction. Holme & King also had a standard gauge loco here and mixed gauge track would appear to be present in this view.* [H D Bowtell Collection]

*Another view of the Manning Wardle* XIT *at work. The more distant steam crane is inscribed 'Holme & King Ltd. Liverpool Nº26".* [Harold D Bowtell Collection]

From the foregoing, it would seem that the branch line from Torpantau in the direction of the reservoirs existed, at the very least, from 1882 until about 1902. The line was not shown on a large scale Ordnance Survey map surveyed in 1904. On a site visit of 2 April 1972, HDB noted "much narrow gauge flat-bottomed rail in the vicinity of the Upper and Lower reservoirs used in edging roads etc".

## Taf Fechan Reservoir, Pontsticill

Empowered by an Act of 1911, Merthyr Corporation let a contract to Sir Robert McAlpine & Sons on 16 June 1913 for the construction of a major earth dam at Pontsticill, close to the B&M Railway station. The dam is at grid reference SO 060119. The contract also provided for various associated works including road diversions on both sides of the valley. The price was to be £232,000. The trench beneath the embankment was to go down to 80ft maximum depth in the valley bottom and to 103ft on the west side. The embankment would be 110ft above the ground and the huge lake would take in the older Pentwyn (or Dolygaer) Reservoir at the northern end of the site. This latter, with a capacity of 346 million gallons, had been built for the Merthyr Board of Health between 1859 and February 1863, although a premature official opening had taken place on 6 October 1862! After some years, serious and persistent leakage was discovered at Pentwyn, a result of the embankment having been built across a major geological fault, despite the Board's Consulting Engineer being the very eminent Thomas Hawkesley. This chronic water loss led directly to the provision of the Lower Neuadd Reservoir described earlier.

By 1912 Pentwyn Reservoir was losing eleven million gallons per day despite previous remedial works. Further repairs were put in hand in 1912/13, reducing the daily loss to 2 million gallons. This was considered acceptable given that construction work was about to start on the new Pontsticill Reservoir, which would incorporate the Pentwyn reservoir and impound its leakage.

*Taf Fechan reservoir after impounding had begun, viewed from near Pontsticill Junction station. Note the mixed (standard and 3 ft) gauge construction track still in situ.* [Taf Fechan WSB]

*Pontsticill Junction station, with signal box to right of the station house, viewed across the reservoir from the west, 19 October 1972. Note the former incline to the quarry on the hillside at extreme left.* [Harold D Bowtell]

Pontsticill was planned to contain 3,290 million gallons, top water level being 1,070ft above ordnance datum (o.d.) - later 3,400 million gallons and 1,082ft. McAlpines made a good start, using 3ft gauge tracks on the actual site and employing at least two narrow gauge locomotives:

34　0-4-0 saddle tank　oc 9in x 15in
　　by Hudswell Clarke 1037 of 1913 - ex works on 25 June 1913 for delivery to McAlpines at Merthyr, nine days after the contract was signed. Later used by them on their Llandarcy Refinery contract at Skewen, W Glamorgan, for the Anglo-Persian Oil Co Ltd, 1917 - 1918; then on their Stornoway job, Western Isles, 1919 - 1922. She was at the North Wales Power Co's Maentwrog hydro-electric reservoir contract, Merioneth, 1924-1928. Numbered 12 for a period later in her life, 1928 - c.1934, she was on numerous other McAlpine jobs, including a spell on the Ebbw Vale steelworks reconstruction in 1937. Later with Paulings, contractors, from 1942 working on their Magnesium Elektron factory contract, Burnley, Lancs, c.1942 - 1943. Finally scrapped by George Bros at Paulings' Crymlyn Burrows depot, Swansea, c.1951.

19　0-4-0 saddle tank　oc 9in x 18in
　　by Andrew Barclay 927 of 1901. This loco was new to Scottish contactor John Paton and used on his Lochearnhead, St. Fillans & Comrie Railway contract for the Caledonian Rly, 1901 - 1902, then passed to William Duncan who took over the contract in 1902 and completed the job in 1905. She was with McAlpines at Clydebank by 6/1912. To Pontsticill, c.1913. Spares were delivered for a Barclay loco to McAlpines at Taf Fechan in 1/1915. (AB 927 was built as a standard gauge/3ft gauge convertible, so she could have been either gauge here.) On McAlpines British Dyes contract, Huddersfield, W. Yorks, by 8/1918 and later on other McAlpine jobs. Declared "obsolete" in 1931. No further trace.

As a result of the outbreak of war, the works on the Taf Fechan were soon suspended and placed under care and maintenance. McAlpines ceased all work in 1917.

*Taf Fechan (Pontsticill) reservoir looking south-west from the former B&MR trackbed 19 October 1972. The Brecon Mountain Railway now reuses this route on its run to Dolygaer.* [H D Bowtell]

Resumption of the project in April 1922 was under the Taf Fechan Water Supply Act of 1921 and in the same year Parliament authorised the formation of the Taf Fechan Water Supply Board, embracing Rhymney Valley Water Board, Pontypridd & Rhondda Joint Water Board, Aberdare UDC and Llantrisant & Llantwit Fardre RDC as well as Merthyr Corporation. Direct control and labour was now employed and the reservoir came to be known as the Taf Fechan Reservoir. A final settlement, at probably £120,000 in all, was made with McAlpines in January 1925, after five years of legal action and negotiations.

Merthyr Corporation had started on site in a small way in 1918 but work recommenced in earnest in about June 1922, with Mr T F Harvey, the Board's Engineer, and Sir Alexander Binnie, Son & Deacon as joint Engineers-in-Chief. (Mr Harvey had worked on the Upper Neuadd project some 25 years earlier). Mr F V Stillingfleet was appointed Resident Engineer. The Abercriban site of Abercriban Quarries Company, which may have been McAlpine's source of puddle clay, was rejected and a site opened up at Pengarnddu to the north of the B&MR station at Dowlais Top, a royalty being paid to Guest, Keen and Nettlefolds. The B&MR was to carry about 60,000 tons of clay from Dowlais Top to Pontsticill over a period of years, at 1/9d per ton. In order to maintain the safety of the decrepit Pentwyn dam for a few more years the GWR (previously B&MR) ran some clay on to Dolygaer, using a locomotive for shuttle trips between trains on the 1¾ miles Pontsticill to Dolygaer section.

A quarter-mile long siding was put in at Dowlais Top for loading the clay trains and the Railway Company's own "heavy locomotives" worked into it. In 1925 the GWR exacted £15 18s 0d from the Board for damage to a locomotive derailed here; the Board's engineer had put up a defence, claiming that the engine was "tight" due to being newly out of workshops and that this had caused the derailment. At Pontsticill, the B&MR had extended their sidings to handle the traffic and the Board provided a standard gauge locomotive to convey the wagons over a temporary line to a staging at the east (Pontsticill station) end of the dam site. A 3ft gauge incline brought the puddle down to the actual works and narrow (3ft) gauge tracks were used on the site, being raised as the bank progressed. The narrow gauge also extended up both sides of the valley, just beneath the future water level, in order to bring material for the bank, which was obtained by the excavations of two steam navvies, one working on each side of the valley bottom; they were Rustons with 2 cu yd and 1½ cu yd capacity buckets. Engine sheds were built in 1922, at Abercriban farm on the east shore north of Pontsticill station, for the fleet of 3ft gauge locomotives. A shed was built on the higher level, near the station, for the new (strictly, reconditioned) standard gauge locomotive received in July 1922.

Quite early on, on 11 November 1922, a wagon of clay became detached from the rope at the incline top and killed a workman, Tom Powell, who was in the puddle trench below. Safety chains were added after this tragedy. Expansion was the order of the day and various McAlpine temporary buildings were demolished and new huts to accommodate the workforce were built, early in 1923. The workshops were below the dam site, near the outlet from the tunnel under the dam. By July 1924, a trestle bridge crossed the Ffrwyd stream at the valve tower and a bridge across the Ffrwyd diversion had been completed; these carried narrow gauge lines. During 1924 - 1925 some 360 to 380 men were at work. In June 1922, 100 narrow gauge wagons were purchased from Nott, Brodie & Co Ltd at Blaen-y-Cwm, near Beaufort and in June 1925 others were bought from Manchester Corporation, surplus after the building of Heaton Park reservoir. There was a hold up of transport of clay to the site and of work on site for a period in May 1926 owing to the General Strike. After resumption, deliveries continued until arrangements for the Dowlais Top sidings were terminated in October 1926. The quarry for most of the necessary stone was on the hill above the B&MR, just north east of Pontsticill station; it was grey granite and was brought down an incline and then "below the station houses". In addition to men living at site, others came from Dowlais daily, a paddy train with B&MR coaches painted chocolate colour, running at 7.30am and returning at 5.30pm.

*Hudswell Clarke 1037 of 1913, 3 ft gauge, was new to McAlpine's (N°.34) for the first phase of the Taf Fechan scheme. This photo is believed to show her on McAlpine's North Orbital Road (A405) contract, Herts, in 1930-31 where she ran on 3 ft. 6 in. gauge tracks.* *[ILS Collection]*

The opening ceremony on completion of the new lake, two and a half miles long, was by Lord Buckland of Bwlch, on 21 July 1927, with some 450 guests present. It is of interest to note that in the course of excavating for the associated pipeline at a location near Abercynon, part of the Merthyr (or Penydarren Ironworks) tramroad of 1802 was found, with cast iron tram plates, each 3ft long, still fixed to stone sleeper blocks. The Board presented rails to both the National Museum of Wales at Cardiff and the Merthyr Tydfil Museum at Cyfarthfa Castle. Details of the locomotives employed by the Taf Fechan Water Supply Board follow:

### Standard gauge

VICTORIA   0-4-0 saddle tank   oc 12in x 18in
> by Hunslet   78 of 1872. This was new to Thomas Richardson & Sons Ltd, West Hartlepool Ironworks, Co. Durham, their N°.4; with Terry Greaves & Co. Ltd., Old Roundwood Colliery, Wakefield, Yorks (WR) by 1/1876 until after 7/1901. She was purchased for Pontsticill in 12/1920 for £2,300 (surely indicating a greatly renewed loco) and was available for sale in 11/1926 and offered at Pontsticill 28/9/1927. To A R Adams & Son, dealers, Newport, Mon, 12/1927; then to Croft Granite, Brick & Concrete Co Ltd, Croft, Leics, 14/8/1930.

TAF FECHAN   0-4-0 saddle tank   oc 12in x 18in.
> by Hudswell Clarke 276 of 1885. New to Charrington & Co. Ltd., Abbey Brewery, Burton-on-Trent, Staffs. Resold by them to the makers, c.1921. Rebuilt by Hudswells in 1922, purchased from them 5/1922 for £1625 and received by the Board by 5/7/1922. She is believed to have been given her name at the site. Driven by David Jones. For sale as for VICTORIA above. To Rossett Sand & Gravels Ltd., Marford, Flints, by 7/1928; later with Cudworth & Johnson, dealers and hirers, Wrexham; eventually to Richard Briggs & Son Ltd's limestone quarry, Chatburn, Lancs, c.1937/38 direct from a hire at Gresford Colliery. Superseded in 1947 and scrapped at Chatburn, c.1949.

*Hudswell Clarke 424 was RUBY on the 3 ft gauge at Pontsticill, but had worked earlier at Aberdare and Blaen y-Cwm reservoirs (both in Chapter 8). Seen here working for Richard Baillie at Ladybower Reservoir, Derbyshire, in the 1930s.*                    *[W H Whitworth]*

**NEWPORT   0-4-0 saddle tank   oc 9in x 15in.**

by Hudswell Clarke 311 of 1889: rebuilt 1915 by H Arnold at Doncaster.  New to William Perch of Cwm Clydach Colliery, Rhondda, 18/4/1889, as CLYDACH, (2ft 10in gauge originally); colliery closed c.1897; with C D Phillips, dealer of Newport, in 1899; To Abram Kellett & Sons HAGLEY (2ft 9in gauge) by 1900 on the Birmingham Corporation pipeline contact; with Harold Arnold & Son by 1908 and was their POTT at Leighton reservoir, Yorkshire, (by then 3ft gauge); and then at Arnold's GNR Colsterworth contract.  To Topham, Jones & Railton, c.1916 and subsequently with Executor of L P Nott building the Newport Graving Dock (hence name) c.1918 and on to Blaen-y-Cwm reservoir near Beaufort c.1919; purchased for Taf Fechan from there 6/1922.   For sale at Pontsticill, 28/9/1927. Later with C D Phillips, dealer, Newport, 4/1929, to United Stone Firms (1926) Ltd, Porthgain, Pembrokeshire, 9/1929; broken up there in 9/1953.

**RUBY   0-4-0 saddle tank   oc 8in x 12in.**

by Hudswell Clarke 424 built in 1894 (but delivered in 1897 and so dated). New to Aberdare UDC. Used by contractor William Jones on the UDC's Nantmoel Reservoir job, Glamorgan, 1897 - 1899, as NANTMELYN (see Ch.8); to William Kennedy, contractor of Partick, Glasgow. Next on John Best's reservoir contract for Falkirk & Larbert Water Trustees at Drumbowie, near Denny, Stirlingshire, 1901 to 1907. Probably at Best's Craigleith Quarry, Edinburgh, in 12/1906 and definitely with John Best on Bolton Corporation's Delph Reservoir job from c.1908 to c.1916. With Henry Boot & Sons (London) Ltd on their Trumpington (MoM) contract, Cambs, c.1918. To Muirhead, McDonald, Wilson & Co Ltd, Fulham depot, London. With Exor. of Nott/Nott, Brodie at Blaen-y-Cwm as RUBY from c.1918 to 1922 (see Ch.8).  Purchased from there 6/1922. Driven at Taf Fechan by Albert Sheldon. For sale at Pontsticill, 28/9/1927. Later, by 4/1929, with A R Adams, the Newport dealer, who sold her to contractor Richard Baillie at East Lothian Water Board's Hopes Reservoir at Gifford, in the Lammermuir Hills, after 6/1931, by 2/1932; later going on to Baillie's Ladybower Reservoir job, Derbys, in 1935, where she ended her days, c.1949/50.

**15 BEAUFORT   0-4-0 saddle tank   oc 8in x 12in.**

by Hudswell Clarke 485 of 1897.   New to Cyfarthfa Iron Works, Merthyr as "15" and sold thence to C D Phillips at Newport in 1915. With Exor. of  Nott/Nott, Brodie at Blaen-y-Cwm. Purchased from there 6/1922. For sale at Pontsticill 28/9/1927. To C D Phillips again by 11/1927; for sale in 8/1928 and eventually sold in 1936 to Consett Iron Co Ltd for their Butsfield quarry, Co. Durham - where HDB saw her working in 9/1950, the year before her demise.  The "15" plate from Cyfarthfa days was still carried.

**LEIGHTON   0-4-0 saddle tank   oc 10in x 14in.**

by Peckett 968 of 1902. Originally CHEESDEN of Heywood and Middleton Water Board, Lancs; with H Arnold in Colsterdale, from 1911 as LEIGHTON; still his property in 10/1914. With Exor of Nott/Nott, Brodie at Blaen-y-Cwm. Purchased from there 6/1922. For sale at Pontsticill, 28/9/1927. Later with A R Adams at Newport by 4/1929; for sale as 3ft gauge until 10/1933 but sold to Edward Curran & Co Ltd, Cardiff, after 3/1935 as standard gauge.

The four 3ft gauge locomotives discussed above were inspected on 15 May 1922 by J W Price, mechanical engineer of Treharris, on behalf of Mr Stillingfleet of the Taf Fechan Water Supply Board; they were placed in steam at the Blaen-y-Cwm reservoir site by Mr Brebner, agent of Nott, Brodie. Their purchase was approved on 7 June 1922 for £1,900.  Also on offer and inspected at the same time was -

**REINDEER**   0-4-0 saddle tank   oc 10in x 16in

by Hudswell Clark 397 of 1892. Rebuilt 1915 at Doncaster by H Arnold. Originally WHITTLE DENE of the Newcastle and Gateshead Water Company. With contractor John Best in Ireland for his Cork, Blackrock & Passage Railway contract, c.1902 - c1904, and from about 1906 at Bradford Corporation's Angram Reservoir in the Yorkshire Dales as ANGRAM; then at his Delph Reservoir job for Bolton, c1908 - c1916 as "N°.21". To Muirhead, MacDonald Wilson & Co Ltd at Fulham Depot and then c.1919 to Blaen-y-Cwm where she became REINDEER. She was described by Mr Price as in the least satisfactory condition and was NOT purchased by the Board, but in c.1924 she turned up as BARNSLEY on Barnsley Corporation's Scout Dike Reservoir project and finished at Derwent Valley Water Board's Ladybower Reservoir in Derbyshire, with Richard Baillie, working there from c.1936, but dismantled by autumn 1938.

*3 ft gauge Montreal Loco Works 54933 of 1917 was an unusual engine at Pontsticill, having come to the UK to assist in the war effort. Obtained via government 'surplus' disposals and later, as seen here in the 1940s, passing to APCM Holborough Cement Works, Kent.*          *[Frank Jones]*

3ft gauge locomotives subsequently acquired were:

**MONTREAL**   0-4-0 saddle tank   oc 9in x 14in.

by Montreal Loco Works 54933 of 1917. Purchased 12/1922 for £650; previously Board of Trade, Timber Supply Dept, Catford Plant Depot, London, where auctioned 20/7/1920. Driven by Mr Cooper at Pontsticill. For sale at Pontsticill, 28/9/1927. Later advertised by Frank Munn, Cardiff dealer, 23/11/1927. Sold in 1928 by R R Paton Ltd, Cardiff (who was associated with Munn and later, by 3/1932, took over his business) to Associated Portland Cement Manufacturers Ltd, Holborough Works, Kent, where she enjoyed a long life. Scrapped there, c.5/1953.

**RHONDDA** 0-4-0 saddle tank oc 10in x 16in.
   by W G Bagnall 2218 of 1923 - came new; in service by 12/1923. For sale at Pontsticill, 2/9/1927. To Lehane, Mackenzie & Shand in 1928; became their HALIFAX at Gorple Reservoirs contract at Hebden Bridge, West Yorks, for Halifax Corporation (contract finished 1934).

**RHYMNEY** 0-4-0 saddle tank oc 10in x 16in.
   by W G Bagnall 2219 of 1923 - came new; in service by 12/1923. For sale at Pontsticill 28/9/1927. To Lehane, Mackenzie & Shand in 1928 - became their TAFF FAWR (note spelling of "Taff") at Gorple.

The two foregoing engines were ordered after visits in August 1923 to Peckett's, Hudswell Clarke's and Bagnall's works: they cost £1,125 each. Both HALIFAX (ex RHONDDA) and TAFF FAWR (ex RHYMNEY) stayed with Lehanes for their Fernilee Reservoir job for Stockport Corporation from c.1932 - 1937. Later they are both believed to have worked with Balfour, Beatty & Co Ltd on wartime construction work on the Orkneys, before finding their way to the Admiralty storeyard at Inverkeithing by 7/1946 and to J N Connell's scrapyard at Coatbridge by 10/1947. They were cut up there sometime between 1950 and 1953. The pair thus seem to have spent their whole working lives together.

**MERTHYR** 0-4-0 saddle tank oc 10in x 16in.
   by W G Bagnall 2233 of 1924 - ordered 4/1924 and received new on 28/7/1924 at a cost of £1,150. Available for disposal (as actually were all the other locos) in 11/1926 but not listed in 1927; believed sold in 1926 to Lehane, Mackenzie & Shand - became their BATLEY at Brownhill Reservoir, Holmbridge, W. Yorks, for Batley Corporation, going on c.1928 to Gorple. Followed the two previous Bagnalls to Fernilee and Inverkeithing, but after WW2 improbably found herself, via Matlock dealer William Twigg, working for the LMS, and later BR, at Beeston sleeper depot, near Nottingham, carrying the number 10 and still with the name BATLEY. Withdrawn from BR stock, 10/1955 and scrapped.

A preliminary announcement by Taf Fechan Water Board of a sale of plant including locos at this site was made in the *Contract Journal*, 1/12/1926. It may be noted that the sale of 28-29 September 1927, advertised in the *Contract Journal*, 7/9/1927 and conducted by Sir Illtyd Thomas, of 17 Quay Street, Cardiff, referred to items displayed at the "Broad Gauge Loco Shed" (sic) and the others "at Abercriban Yard near the Upper Loco Sheds"; this last would be the narrow gauge sheds, described to HDB as near Abercriban farm, a little north of Pontsticill station and probably just above the present high water level, in the woodland on the bank of the lake. A corrugated iron shed 56ft by 28ft was probably for these narrow gauge locomotives and the 28ft by 26ft shed could be the standard gauge depot more closely adjoining the station. A hauling engine with two 10in x 18in cylinders and drum, made by John Wood & Sons Ltd of Wigan, was at the quarry, doubtless installed at the incline head. One steam navvy (N°.10) was sold before completion of the works, going to Macclesfield Corporation, and the other was surplus by November 1926.

In connection with the Pontsticill (Taf Fechan) Reservoir project, contractors C V Buchan & Co Ltd won a contract to lay a pipeline from the reservoir to Cardiff. Work took place between 1925 and 1927. A small, presumably narrow gauge, steam locomotive and a petrol locomotive are recorded as working near Aberfan (south of Merthyr Tydfil).

It is interesting to note that in the *Contract Journal*, 2/2/1921, the following advertisement appeared: Wanted 2ft gauge loco, not less than 6 x 9 - Merthyr Corporation Reservoir Works, Pontsticill, near Merthyr Tydfil.

Bagnall 2218 of 1923 was the first of three handsome 10in locos supplied new to the Water Board for the 3ft gauge lines at Taf Fechan and was then named RHONDDA, but our photo shows her as HALIFAX on Lehane, Mackenzie & Shand's Fernilee job. [A C Baker Collection]

Bagnall 2219 was RHYMNEY at Taf Fechan and later became TAFF FAWR when with Lehane, Mackenzie and Shand. Seen here at Fernilee.
[G J Hill Collection]

Bagnall 2233 of 1924 was MERTHYR at Taf Fechan, then BATLEY with Lehanes.She had the unlikely honour of later becoming a part of the British Railways locomotive fleet.
[R W Miller Collection]

*All three photographs are believed to have been taken by the late W H Whitworth on 10 Feb 1934 at Fernilee.*

# Chapter 4

## Cray and other projects for Swansea Corporation and Ystradfellte for Neath Rural District Council

The private Swansea Waterworks Company was formed by an Act of Parliament of 1837 but it achieved little. A very severe outbreak of cholera killed 133 in 1849, not surprising since only 1,100 houses (in a town of some 30,000 population) had water supply by 1850. In 1852 the Local Board of Health obtained an Act to construct their own works for supplying the town. They bought two small reservoirs at Brynmill and Cwmdonkin from the company. These soon proved inadequate and in 1854 the Board called upon the services of Robert Rawlinson as Consulting Engineer. In 1859, as water shortage became desperate, three new dams were proposed on the Lliw, Blaen-nant-Ddu and Llan rivers, and four service reservoirs in the town. An Act for these works obtained the Royal Assent in 1860, though the Llan reservoir seems never to have been built. Rawlinson was appointed Engineer–in–Chief for the project. He recommended that work on the Lliw and Blaen-nant-Ddu reservoirs be commenced urgently, but was over-ruled by the cost conscious local board who decided that Lliw alone be proceeded with, construction starting in 1862. With hindsight this proved to be a great mistake. In the event, work at Blaen-nant-Ddu was not initiated until 1874. Work on a second (Upper) Lliw dam did not start until 1886. These early projects are briefly described later in this chapter, but first we will consider Swansea's great enterprise at Cray.

## Cray

As work on the Upper Lliw Reservoir (see the notes following) drew near an end, Swansea Corporation secured an Act in 1892 for a dam at grid reference SN 884221 on the river Crai to form a reservoir on the Brecon side of the watershed. The main access to the site in those days was by the Neath and Brecon Railway, which climbed the Tawe valley past Craig-y-Nos (Penwyllt) station to its bleak crossing place and signal box at Bwlch Summit, 1,267ft; then dropping north eastwards down the Crai valley. The reservoir site was on the left, below the line, between the summit and Cray station. A siding was put in near the site. The N&BR had been opened in 1867 and came into the GWR group on 1 July 1922 but its main line east of Colbren Junction was worked from 1877 by the Midland Railway (LMSR from 1923) until the withdrawal of the LMS passenger service between Swansea St. Thomas and Brecon from 1 January 1931. After that GWR passenger trains, three each way daily, began to run through between Neath Riverside and Brecon. Through LMS goods workings to Swansea ceased in September 1932. All traffic east of Craig-y-Nos ended from 15 October 1962 and the line past Cray finally closed.

In the days when Cray Reservoir was built, passenger trains would be made up of smart red carriages and spotless red Johnson 0-4-4 side tank engines, whilst Midland six-coupled tender engines would pass hauling goods trains, probably from Birmingham to Swansea, perhaps even from Somers Town, St Pancras. The Midland Railway's passenger trains in 1904, during the era of Cray waterworks construction, left Swansea at 8.05am, 11.05am and 3.35pm, Monday to Saturday, the first two with through carriages to Birmingham. From Brecon departures for Swansea were at 8.10am, 11.25am and 5.55pm. A spot check in *Bradshaw* for 1887 and 1910 shows almost the same timings, and the GWR trains in and out of Brecon in 1938 were in essentially the same paths.

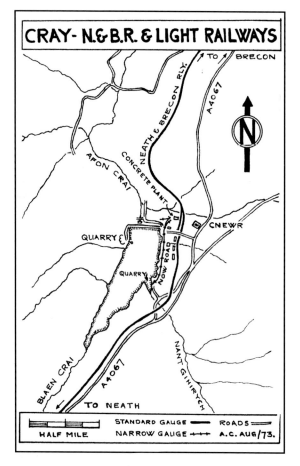

**CRAY- N.& B.R. & LIGHT RAILWAYS**

STANDARD GAUGE ▬▬  ROADS ▭▭
NARROW GAUGE ┼┼┼  A.C. AUG/73.
HALF MILE

Work on the Cray dam began in June 1898 but there were many difficulties with its foundations; the reservoir was not officially opened, by Councillor David Harris, Mayor of Swansea, until 2 October 1907. The firm of John Paterson & Sons Ltd of Glasgow was the successful bidder, their tender of £255,747 11s 6d being accepted in March 1898. They began work in June. Standard gauge sidings connecting with the Neath & Brecon Railway at the north of the site about two miles south of Cray station were in place by July 1899. Patersons ran into difficulties, which resulted in the Corporation buying them out in June 1901 for £26,000, a sum that suggests that a relatively small amount of the work had been carried out. The Corporation then took over the works themselves and completed the job. G H Hill & Sons, of Manchester, were the corporation's consultants and D Kitchingman was Resident Engineer. The Corporation's site manager was Basil Mackenzie, later to be a partner in that well-known firm of reservoir builders, Lehane, Mackenzie & Shand. The "walking ganger" (or general foreman) was H White. (Mackenzie and White went on to fill the same roles at Stockport Corporation's Kinder Reservoir, Derbyshire, from 1907.) The construction of the dam was unusual, mass concrete bonded round heavy stones and faced on both sides in blue bricks, giving it an austere appearance. The dam is 1,250ft long, the foundations go down to 863.5ft above o.d., the top water level is at 1,001ft and the top of the dam at 1,007.5ft, whilst the capacity of the lake is 1,007 million gallons.

An interesting feature was the building of Bwlch tunnel, 5ft high, 3ft 6in wide and 2¾ miles long. This provides the outlet through the watershed to the pipeline down the Tawe Valley to the service reservoirs at Townhill (an open reservoir of 3 million gallons capacity) and at Morriston, both on the approaches to Swansea. One third of this tunnel is below the bed of the lake. Direct labour was employed by the Corporation for the main part of the work. Most of the stone came from a quarry near the south east corner of the lake site and the Corporation used a 3ft gauge railway, roughly parallel to the N&B line but a little lower and about three quarters of a mile in length, to reach the concrete plant and the dam. A smaller quarry was on the west bank, not far from the dam. Dressed stone was brought by rail from Penwyllt quarry, a short distance to the south on the N&B line. The blue bricks would also have come in by rail, possibly from Staffordshire, and cement would have been a significant rail traffic. Provision shops for workpeople were in the area between the road (now a major one, much realigned and widened, but then insignificant) and the N&BR. The living huts were said to be lower down this side of the valley.

Four 3ft gauge locomotives have been identified in Swansea Corporation ownership:

*Cray Reservoir from the east, with the valve tower left of centre and the dam at right, 25/5/2004*
*[Geoffrey Hill]*

CRAY   0-4-0 saddle tank   oc 7in x12in

    by W G Bagnall 1674 of 1901 – came new here, delivered 12/1901 as CRAY to the order of the Corporation. Spares were supplied to Swansea until 5/1906. Later with James Byrom Ltd, on Scout Moor Reservoir contract, Ramsbottom, Lancs, (for Bury & District Joint Water Board) probably from late 1906 - 1909. Byrom received spares for this locomotive as late as 7/1914, but no location is known. Possibly with Harold Arnold & Son building Leighton Reservoir, Masham, for Leeds Corporation, but this is not confirmed. There is a strong suggestion that she may have been the 7in Bagnall with Baguley valve gear subsequently photographed in WW1 in use by soldiers of the Canadian Forestry Corps on timber felling work. No further trace. [It is interesting to note that Hudswell Clarke 1086 of 1914 also bore the name CRAY-- from c.1925 in the ownership of contractors Lehane, Mackenzie & Shand. This may commemorate Basil Mackenzie's important role in the earlier construction of Cray reservoir. ]

PENWYLLT   0-4-0 saddle tank   oc 7in x 12in

    by W G Bagnall 1704 of 1902 - came new in 12/1902 as PENWYLLT, to the order of the Corporation, and was still here in 10/1905 (when rather surprisingly a new boiler was ordered from the makers).  By 3/1906 she was with Harold Arnold, believed at the Castle Carrock (Carlisle Corporation) and Leighton (Leeds Corporation) reservoir contracts. Arnolds received spares until 7/1913. She was later with the Harris and Lewis Welfare and Development Company in the Hebrides; and later still with A M Carmichael, Edinburgh contractors. Auctioned on their behalf at West Craigs Quarry, Corstorphine, 4-6/5/1938. To J Hunter Jnr  (a scrap merchant?).

SWANSEA   0-4-0 saddletank   oc 8in x 12in

    by Peckett 959 of 1902 - came new to order of Swansea Corporation leaving the makers in Bristol, 30/5/1902, for Cray.  Later with Harold Arnold, just possibly at Embsay Moor contract, certainly at his Castle Carrock and Leighton Reservoir jobs, Ripon Camp construction and Colsterworth (GNR) contracts.  By 4/1919 she was with Cafferata & Co Ltd on their Hawton Tramway at Newark and scrapped there in 1947.

*The 3ft gauge* PENWYLLT *(Bagnall 1704 of 1902) worked at Cray but is here seen, probably in the late 1930s, at contractor A M Carmichael's yard at Corstorphine, Edinburgh.* [A C Baker Collection]

*A Peckett 'official' portrait of works' number 959* SWANSEA *before final painting and supply new to the Corporation in May 1902.* [Peter Michie Collection]

*With 10" cylinders* LITTLE DON *(Peckett 699 of 1897) was the largest locomotive used at Cray. Seen here with her first owner, Sheffield Corporation, at Langsett Reservoir in the Little Don valley, West Riding.* [Harold D Bowtell Collection]

LITTLE DON   0-4-0 saddle tank   oc
> believed to be 10in x 14in, by Peckett 699 of 1897. Built new for Sheffield Corporation's Langsett Reservoir project, W. Yorks, and purchased 6/1904 by Swansea Corporation from Sheffield Corporation for £500.  Later the property of Preston Corporation at Spade Mill N°.1 Reservoir construction, Longridge, Lancs, probably from 5/1908; from c.1910 belonging to McDonnell and Deakin, contractors, at Burnley Corporation's Hurstwood Reservoir contract and then staying with Burnley Corporation.

In *Machinery Market*,  30/3/1906, Evans Bros Ltd, engineers of Morriston & Swansea offered for sale "three three-foot gauge locomotives, 7inch, 8inch and 10inch". From the loco histories presented here these would be CRAY, SWANSEA and LITTLE DON respectively. Two locomotives were advertised in the *Contract Journal* of 25/7/1906 and one in the 29/1/1908 edition. The likelihood is that the first refers to CRAY and LITTLE DON and the second to LITTLE DON, which seems to have been the last to leave.

The Midland Railway working timetable of October 1904 identified "Cray Waterworks" as a location.  Going down, the 12.55pm out of Brecon goods station for Penwyllt left Cray station at 3.20pm and stopped at Cray Waterworks siding; it was booked to leave there at 3.50pm and reach Penwyllt at 4.25pm. A 5.20pm goods left Penwyllt for Swansea, presumably in part the same train. There was a 10.30am freight from Swansea, due at Penwyllt 5.05pm and a 5.50pm thence to Brecon goods station (8.50pm), calling at Cray Waterworks siding, and departing at 7.08pm. Curiously, the timetable marked the down trains "Goods" and the up ones "Mineral". They would put off wagons of cement, bricks, pipes, valves and the like and no doubt brought the stone which came from Penwyllt quarry to the site of the works.

In January 1895 the Corporation let a contract for the construction of the 23½ mile pipeline (referred to earlier) down the Tawe valley to the Swansea service reservoirs. The contractors were the well-known firm of Lucas & Aird. Later, in 1909, after the completion of the Cray Reservoir, Lucas & Aird were called on to construct a second pipeline to Swansea and then in 1911, seemingly, to carry out further work on the service reservoir at Morriston. No locomotives are known on these contracts, but their use must be a possibility.

# Notes on other Swansea Corporation projects

## *Lower Lliw Reservoir*

Robert Rawlinson's plans for the Lliw dam (authorised by the 1860 Act) and an earthenware pipeline thence to Swansea were accepted by the Board of Health in 1861. The dam itself, at grid reference SN 648034, comprised contract N°.1 of the project. William Williams of Swansea was the successful bidder, his price £27,449 5s 8d. Work started in March 1862 with Hugh Unsworth appointed by Rawlinson as Resident Engineer. It was an earth bank dam, at 82ft one of the highest of its type at the time, and was to hold back almost 300 million gallons. Top water level was 410ft above o.d.. At completion in 1867 total expenditure on the reservoir, pipeline and supply arrangements was £76,600. The dam suffered leaks and subsidence from 1873 necessitating repairs and this hastened the construction of the Blaen-nant-Ddu reservoir. Leaks occurred again in 1883, but the reservoir continued in use until 1975, albeit at reduced capacity. The aging dam was replaced by a new structure in 1976 - 1978 giving a capacity of 290 million gallons as part of the West Glamorgan Water Board's River Towy abstraction scheme. (The Water Board had taken control, from 1/10/1966, of the water undertakings of Swansea, Neath and Port Talbot as well as those of six surrounding rural and urban districts, including Neath Rural District Council - see under Ystradfellte Reservoir later in the chapter.) The reservoir became known as Lower Lliw following the promotion of an Upper Lliw reservoir from 1884. No information is as yet available concerning the use of railways at Lower Lliw.

For a detailed account of the construction of the Lower Lliw reservoir and the troublesome aftermath see *Early Victorian Water Engineers* by G. M. Binnie (Thomas Telford, 1981)

## *Blaen-nant-Ddu Reservoir*

A contract for this 127 million gallon reservoir at Felindre (grid reference SN 640035), authorised by an Act of 1873, was let in August 1874 to W R Geen (or Geen & Dickon) of Birmingham at a price of £43,700. Design and supervision of the works was entrusted to Edward Cousins, the Town Surveyor. The work took longer than expected and cost twice the original contract sum as a result of the need for a very deep trench for the dam foundation and problems with natural springs. Completion was eventually achieved in 1878. Seepage of water into mine workings below the reservoir had become such a problem by 1919 that the reservoir was drained. After repairs, Blaen-nant-Ddu continued to serve the people of Swansea until 1954. Not a great deal is known about the construction phase but a 3ft 3in gauge locomotive used by Geen at the site has been identified. This was probably employed on a tramway 2½ miles long that almost certainly brought clay to the site from Abergelli clay pits. This locomotive was:

- 0-4-0 saddle tank   oc 10in x 16in
  by Manning Wardle 639 of 1877 - new to Geen at Swansea. The makers made an arrangement to carry the loco for nine miles on the highway to the site.  The loco was offered for sale from 8/1878, to be auctioned 3-5/10/1878 (*The Builder*, 28/9/1878) and in *The Engineer*, 30/7/1880, by one Philip Rogers. She passed to the Glamorgan Coal Co Ltd at Penrhiwfer Colliery, Penygraig, Mid Glamorgan, c.1880 and enjoyed quite a long career there before being offered at auction in 6/1896 (*Colliery Guardian*, 29/5/1896).  No further trace is recorded.

# Upper Lliw Reservoir

*Building News* of 12/3/1886 reported that contractors Baldry & Yerburgh, of London SW1, had secured a contract from Swansea Corporation for the construction of the Upper Lliw Reservoir, two miles up the valley from Lower Lliw, at Felindre (grid reference SN 661059). The works were authorised by an Act of 1884. The price was £65,835. Work was completed and the reservoir brought into use on 12 October 1894. The dam was of the earth bank type and the top water level was 614ft above o.d.. The capacity of the reservoir was quoted as 298 million gallons in the 1970s. No locomotives can definitely be associated with this job, but the contractors owned a locomotive named LLIW (or possibly "LNW"), which was being repaired by Markham & Co, of Chesterfield, Derbyshire, in February 1891.

# Usk Reservoir

This large reservoir of 2,700 million gallons is situated south of the A40 Brecon – Llandovery road about 3½ miles west of the village of Trecastle. The reservoir is partly in Dyfed and partly in Powys (1974 boundaries and names). The dam, at grid reference SN 833288, is of earth with a puddle core. Work commenced in about 1950 and completion was in 1955. The main contractor was Richard Costain Limited of London.  Binnie, Deacon & Gourley of Westminster were the Consulting Engineers, Mr Trevelyan Price was the Borough Water Engineer and Manager and the Chief Resident Engineer was Mr L B Aylen.

A notable feature of the project was a supply tunnel, 2,370 yards long, from the reservoir, under Mynydd Myddfai, to reach the Swansea side of the watershed. From here a ten-mile-long pipeline carried the water to Bryngwyn treatment works, two miles south-east of Llandeilo. Another nine miles of pipeline took the supply to Graig Fawr break-pressure tank south of Ammanford. From here the piped supply was routed to two underground service reservoirs of 2½ million gallons each, one at Cockett, west of the city, the other at Clase, to the north-east. John Morgan (Builders) Ltd of Cardiff built Cockett Reservoir and John Howard & Co Ltd of London, the Clase Reservoir. The cost of the entire scheme was £3,108,000. The dam is 1,575ft long and 109ft high. The crest of the weir is 1,006ft above o.d.. The reservoir was inaugurated by HM Queen Elizabeth II, accompanied by HRH the Duke of Edinburgh, on 6 August 1955.

A photograph taken on 6/4/1953 shows two narrow gauge diesel locomotives emerging from a tunnel at the site, probably the supply tunnel. Other photographs of the site show no evidence of railway use on the surface for earthmoving or dam building. Ruston & Hornsby supplied two new 2ft gauge diesel locomotives, numbers 297056-57, to Richard Costain on 5/12/1950. They were type 30DL with four wheels, weighed 3¼ tons and very probably the locos used at Usk. Any additional information on the tunneling railway here would be most welcome.

# Ystradfellte

About two miles westward from the Beacons Reservoir of Cardiff Corporation, but separated from it by the slopes of the 2,400ft Fan Fawr, is Ystradfellte (pronounced "Ustradvechte") Reservoir, a narrow lake about three quarters of a mile long in the remote Dringarth Valley. The dam is at grid reference SN 945174. A standard gauge railway of some seven miles was built to reach it and 3ft gauge lines were used at the site of construction.

The project had interesting origins. It was promoted by the Neath RDC who administered the largest Rural District in the United Kingdom, embracing sixteen parishes in Glamorgan and one in Brecknock, in the valleys of the Neath, Dulais and Afan rivers and extending to Swansea Bay - a mainly industrial territory. Their sources of water were local and unreliable but they had an energetic engineer, D M Davies, who was determined to change this, and succeeded. He has been described as a tyrant but (however that may be) he could certainly make up his mind and see a job through; and later was noted for the papers he read at conferences to prove it. A scheme by Manserghs of Westminster, Consulting Engineers, for a masonry dam in the adjoining Llia valley was turned down as extravagant. The Dringarth valley was selected. Mr Davies and his staff made the surveys in association with William Fox of Westminster, who was retained as consulting engineer until the council's Act for the works received assent on 1 August 1902. This was the first time that a RDC had secured an Act for the construction of water works. The necessary land was purchased for £6,000 from the Commoners of the Great Forest of Brecon as surface owners, and the mineral rights were obtained for £1,150 from Lord Tredegar as Lord of the Manor.

Design of the works and supervision were by the well-known firm of G H Hill and Sons of Manchester, with Mr W S Becher as their Resident Engineer. An earth embankment was formed largely from material within the future reservoir. The embankment is 920ft long, with its top 114ft above the bed of the stream and the water capacity as completed is around 700 million gallons, the top water level being 1,204ft above o.d.. Cement for concrete was from the South Wales Portland Cement Co at Penarth and therefore involved considerable rail haulage. Silica stone for use in the concrete was obtained three miles downstream from the site and it was hoped to get puddle clay from Cilhepste Coed, also a few miles south of the site, but in practice the quality fell off and 36,000 cubic yards of clay had to be brought by rail from Neath marshes.

The scheme also provided a "break pressure reservoir" of three million gallons to relieve pressure on the mains in the Neath valley and six small covered reservoirs to aid local distribution, at Pontneathvaughan, Resolven, Aberdulais, Tynwaun, Onllwyn and Pantsais.

The dam site was two miles from a public road; the first half-mile being on an inferior farm lane and the rest of the way being merely open mountain. A private road was made over this couple of miles, but the nine-mile route from Great Western Railway's Hirwain station (the township is nowadays Hirwaun) over inadequate public roads and culminating in this private road, was considered quite unsuitable for road motor or steam haulage. Mr Davies favoured a standard gauge railway, fit for main line rolling stock. The Aberdare Canal Tramway ran from Hirwain station northwards for about two miles to Penderyn, where there were (and are) stone quarries. The tramway had been opened in 1786 and was originally owned by Samuel Glover of Abercarn (Monmouthshire) and Birmingham; the engineer being James Dadford. It was a horse tram road with edge rails. It was rebuilt as a plateway by 1809, according to the late Bertram Baxter, who quotes a gauge of 3ft 2in. The Aberdare Canal Company reconstructed it in 1904 with railway permanent way to standard gauge; it is not clear whether it had been made into standard gauge before this.

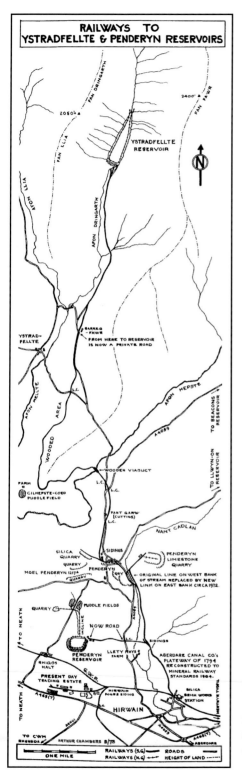

The RDC finally agreed, in March 1905, to build a railway of their own for nearly seven miles northwards from Penderyn, as an extension of the older line. The first part of their route was not within the scope of their Water Act so they adopted a wayleave technique and obtained the land needed "by agreement for a period sufficient for the construction of the works". The route is shown on the accompanying map. The Canal Company's line approached Penderyn on the left of the road from Hirwaun (the line was moved to the right of the road in about 1972 in conjunction with road realignment and widening) and then swung across the road to the quarry. At this point the private line continued on the left (west) of the road, passed close by the corner of the Lamb Hotel (which bears the date 1829) and along the verge through Penderyn village main street, where the local women would beg hot water from the locomotive injector overflow in the tradition familiar on steam railways in the East. The Jerusalem chapel (1857) was on the left of the line, which continued out into fields, a marshalling yard being built here, on the north-west outskirts of the village. (The route thus far remained in use until around 1939 to reach a quarry of the Hirwain Silica Brickworks, the Penderyn Quarries locomotive traversing it to handle the Brickworks' traffic.) Continuing north, the RDC's line crossed the road - the main road from Hirwaun to Brecon - by an oblique level crossing with gates. Its route to the right of the road can be identified by a deep cutting and embankment on a bleak hillside. Beyond the now-widened fork in the road it re-crossed the Brecon main road and also the lesser road, both on the level, and continued through a shallow cutting to the spectacular timber viaduct (illustrated on next page), 300ft long and 50ft above the Hepste river. This bridge was built by an unknown contractor in fourteen weeks and cost £1,257.

The next section is severely curved, much now in woodlands, and probably the ruling gradient of the line -- 1 in 28 for one hundred yards through a cutting -- would be on this portion, which also deviated to serve the Cilhepste clay field. The upper two miles were on farm and private roads, on the east bank of the Dringarth river and well above it. Virtually the whole journey from Penderyn involved steady climbing and at the site the standard gauge eventually climbed to the top level of the reservoir embankment. The railway was built for £13,000 (apart from land) and when it was later dismantled the Council sold the materials for £10,000.

WORKMENS TRAIN EN ROUTE FOR
YSTRADFELLTE WATERWORKS

*Two commercial postcards were produced showing Morrison & Mason's standard gauge workmen's trains crossing the very fine Hepste viaduct.* **Above** *a somewhat damaged card shows* CARDIFF *(Avonside 1401 of 1899) on a northbound train.* **Below** *the locomotive is Hunslet 267 of 1882 with a southbound working.* *[Richard Evans Collection]*

Morrison and Mason Ltd, of Glasgow, were contracted to build the reservoir for £88,932 and work commenced in October 1907. The forecast time for the job was four years but this was exceeded and the eventual cost was £108,755. A temporary supply of water was obtained in April 1913 and the permanent supply was officially inaugurated on 4 April 1914, with full completion of the contract at the end of that year, just in time to avoid being held up by World War 1. Apart from any loads out of Penderyn quarries, from Cilhepste clay field or the silica site, all traffic was brought up from Hirwain station to Penderyn by the Penderyn Quarries locomotive and then taken over by one of Morrison and Mason's engines. A "Paddy Mail" was similarly worked daily from Hirwaun and taken over at Penderyn. At least six second-hand carriages were acquired for this duty.

With the formation of the West Glamorgan Water Board, on 1 October 1966, ownership of the reservoir passed from the RDC to the new body, with headquarters in Swansea.

Four standard gauge locomotives have been more or less identified, of which three belonged to the contractors Morrison & Mason and were all "route engines", that is, they worked throughout the length of the Council's railway –

PROGRESS   0-4-0 tank
　　possibly by Kerr Stuart; the first loco to come here, she probably belonged to the RDC and was employed on building the line. No other details known.

CARDIFF   0-6-0 saddle tank   oc 14in x 20in
　　by Avonside 1401 of 1899 - New for Topham, Jones and Railton's Queen Alexandra Dock contract, Cardiff, 1899-7/1907 as 16 CARDIFF. This loco is believed to have come to Ystradfellte from TJR's Dumballs Road plant depot, Cardiff, between 1/1908 and 10/1910. Morrison & Mason ordered spares for the loco between 7/10/1910 and 10/4/1914. For sale, 25/5/1915 (Contract Journal, 19/5/1915); stated to have been sold to Aberpergwm Colliery at nearby Glyn Neath, though definitely with Taylor's Navigation Steam Coal Co. at Nantgarw Colliery, Taffs Well, still as CARDIFF by 9/1918. Later with Cribbwr Fawr Collieries Ltd., Newlands Colliery, Kenfig Hill, Glam, until after 1/1930 (although not recalled by "gaffers" there to HDB); then to A R Adams & Son, the Newport dealers, and finally to the Crippins Colliery, Lancs, of the Brynn Hall Colliery Co Ltd, as PHYLLIS by 4/1934. She was still here at the closed colliery in 1946 (and later) but never became NCB property. (At Crippins she carried the plate AE 1565/11 that rightly belonged to a 4-coupled loco which Adams acquired in 1934 from Roads Reconstruction Ltd in Somerset. AE 1401 presumably acquired this plate in error during repairs at Adams' yard.).

■ 0-6-0 saddle tank   ic 13in x 18in
　　by Hunslet 267 of 1882 - New to Lucas & Aird, contractors at Hull, building the Hull & Barnsley Rly, 1881-1885. She is known to have been with M&M by 11/1900 (spares records) so will have worked somewhere else for them before here. For sale, 25/5/1915; stated to be sold to Rock Colliery, at nearby Glyn Neath, Glam, but known to have been at Penhydd Colliery (of Penhydd Colliery Co Ltd) also at Glyn Neath, by 2/1923. No trace thereafter. There is a suggestion that this loco was named TIGER at some point while at Ystradfellte.

TRUDY   0-6-0 saddle tank.
　　by Hunslet – almost certainly Hunslet 574 of 1893, which was 11in x 15in oc with small wheels, a bent over weatherboard and cab roof and Hunslet-type TRUDY nameplates. New to S Pearson's Port Talbot Docks and Railway job, Glam, until c.1897 and then worked on his Wootton Bassett-Patchway railway construction (GWR Badminton line), opened in 1903. HDB heard it suggested by a loco man who had been on that contract that TRUDY had been intended for a narrow gauge line, Sudan 3ft 6in gauge suggested. M&M acquired her by 5/1903 so, again, used her somewhere else before here. The loco was still with Sir William Arrol & Co. Ltd, Dunglas, Scotland (who absorbed M&M in 1920), in 1921.

*The standard gauge Avonside 1401 (formerly* CARDIFF*) again, this time in close-up at Crippins Colliery, Lancs, in 1946 near the end of a hard life.* [Frank Jones]

*3 ft gauge Barclay 839 (N°.4) and 840 (N°.5) both worked at Ystradfellte. Here they are seen earlier on the Rhayader pipeline contract in Mid Wales.* [R W Miller Collection]

The 3ft gauge layout was around the dam and extended for a mile or so to the north up each side of the valley, conveying trucks of spoil excavated by steam navvies from the slopes, which were doubtless tipped to form the dam embankment as work progressed. The locomotives were varied in type and origin and the following have been recalled or reported –

N°.4    0-4-0 side tank   oc 6½in x 12in
    by Andrew Barclay 839 of 1898 -  new to M&M on the Rhayader pipeline, Mid Wales.   To Ystradfellte from hire to McLaughlin & Harvey's Kinlochleven contract (British Aluminium Co Ltd), from 4/1907 to 2/1909 at least; then went on from Ystradfellte, by 12/1914, to M&M's Lower Laithe Reservoir contract near Haworth, W Yorks; next to the Old Kilpatrick contract in Dunbartonshire by 10/1918 but back to Lower Laithe by 12/1919. She eventually was sold to John Best & Sons (Edinburgh) Ltd in 6/1925.

N°.5    0-4-0 side tank   oc 6½in x 12in
    by Andrew Barclay 840 of 1899 - delivered new to M&M, at LNWR Knighton goods yard, Shropshire, on 30/5/1899, for work on the Bucknell-Ludlow section of Birmingham Corporation's Rhayader pipeline; she moved in 1908 to Ystradfellte. She was known here as "The Pig" (variant of "The Pug"?) and driven by Walt Nicholas. On completion, sold (on 25/5/1915?) to dealer C D Phillips of Newport and resold 11/1916 to the British Aluminium Company at Foyers on Loch Ness. Presented in 1964 by that company to the Scottish Railway Preservation Society, by whom preserved, initially at Falkirk and more recently at Bo'ness. [Both AB 839 and 840 had worked for a spell in Scotland (from 1903 - 1904 and between the Rhayader and Ystradfellte jobs) on M&M's contract for the Maidens & Dunure Light Rly (Alloway Jn – Girvan), Ayrshire].

*Barclay 1173 of 1909 was one of a pair of six-coupled side tanks that came new to Ystradfellte. Seen here on another M&M job (for Keighley Corporation) at Lower Laithe, West Yorks in 1925 with H Bentley (Bradford) Ltd's  McLaren road locomotive (w/n 1571).   [H D Bowtell Collection]*

- **0-6-0 side tank   oc 7in x 14in**

  by Andrew Barclay 1172 of 1909 - new here in 2/1909. Probably transferred c.1914 to M&M's Lower Laithe contract, West Yorks, (definitely worked there). Sir Wm Arrol & Co Ltd took over this contract in 3/1923 and the loco was here until the final sale in 6/1925. No trace thereafter.

- **0-6-0 side tank   oc 7in x 14in**

  by Andrew Barclay 1173 of 1909 - new here to M&M in 2/1909. Probably transferred c.1914 to Lower Laithe site (definitely worked there) and in the final sale, 6/1925. With John Best at his Portobello Power Station, Edinburgh, contract, c.1929 - 1931; thereafter with A M Carmichael on the North Ballachulish - Fort William - Inverness road contract 1930-1934 and the Carsphairn Dam job, Kirkcudbrightshire, (for Galloway Water Power Co), 1934-1936. A loco answering this description was on offer in Carmichael's big auction at West Craigs Quarry, Corstorphine, Edinburgh, 4-6 May 1938. No further trace.

- **0-4-0 saddle tank   oc 8in x 12in**

  by W G Bagnall 1639 of 1900 - had been new with Enoch Tempest at Walshaw Dean in Yorkshire, as LIPSCOMB - probably handled by A R Adams of Newport in 1909 before use by M&M at Ystradfellte. Subsequently (by 1919) probably on hire to Mountain Ash UDC's Penderyn Reservoir project (which see, Ch. 5), also reached from the Aberdare Canal Company's railway. Later in 1920 back with M&M at Lower Laithe, passing to Sir Wm Arrol & Co Ltd and from 6/1925 with John Best and Richard Baillie.

Additional unidentified 3ft gauge locomotives:

Two 4-coupled locos  (M&M N°.3 and another) are recalled as big locomotives for the narrow gauge, with cylinders about 10in diameter and built by Black Hawthorn; said to be "in good nick". They were not in the sale of 25/5/1915.  However a known M&M N°.3 on another contract was an 0-4-0ST with oc 9in x 15in (so could be considered large for the gauge) by Hudswell Clarke, 865 of 1908, new to Stockport Corporation and acquired by M&M in 8/1911 via dealer Francis B Welch & Co before passing to John Spencer & Sons Ltd, Newburn by 1917, so she could have been at Ystradfellte. She went later to T W Ward Ltd in 1927, then to contractor Richard Baillie by 1931 for reservoir construction at Hopes (East Lothian) and in 1935 at Ladybower (Derbyshire).  The only other large narrow gauge locomotive owned by Morrison & Mason was Andrew Barclay 1133 of 1907 but this was an 0-6-0T although with oc 10in x 18in and is said to have been sent new to the Chew Valley Reservoir contract, West Yorks (for Stalybridge Corporation). As this did not start until about 1910 there was ample time for her to have gone to Ystradfellte first.

Two locomotives attributed to Kerr, Stuart & Co Ltd were recalled erroneously as former Birmingham steam tram engines (converted from 3ft 6in gauge?), rebuilt with cabs.  This identification is not supported by Dr Whitcombe's classic paper *The History of the Steam Tram* and it seems reasonably certain that there were three 0-4-0 side tank locos for 3ft gauge here of the quaint "Sirdar" design with outside cylinders, inside motion, domeless boilers and cab roofs on columns.  Morrison and Mason had three of these delivered new for work on the Rhayader to Birmingham (Elan Valley) pipeline, namely

| N°. 6 | 0-4-0T | oc | 6in x 10in | KS 644 of 1899 - new to Ludlow |
| N°. 7 | 0-4-0T | oc | 6in x 10in | KS 651 of 1899 - new to Ludlow |
| N°. 9 | 0-4-0T | oc | 6½in x 10in | KS 706 of 1900 - new to Cleobury Mortimer |

Photographic evidence shows one of these locos (N°.6) to have a dropped footplate and front running plate.

Three engines fitting the above descriptions were included in the plant sale of 5/1915 and all three were in 6/1915 reported with C D Phillips, the Newport dealer, as "EMLYN N°s.124, 125 and 126" respectively, so there is little doubt they were all at Ystradfellte.  KS 651 and 706 duly passed (evidently via dealer William Jones early in 1916) to Balfour Beatty & Co Ltd at their Kinlochleven contract of 1915-19, Scotland; while KS 644 was later with Croft Granite, Brick & Concrete Co Ltd,

Croft, Leics) from 8/1916. KS 651 was subsequently owned by Wm Tawse Ltd, and used on his Invercannie Reservoir contract, Aberdeenshire, 1920 - 26, and was later with contractor A M Carmichael Ltd of Corstorphine, Midlothian, until scrapped in 1936.

The final sale of contractors' plant was conducted on behalf of Morrison and Mason and held at Penderyn on 25 May 1915 (see *Contract Journal*, 19/5/1915). Items in the catalogue included six railway carriages with four compartments in each, various vehicles for standard and 3ft gauges, two steam navvies, track work, corrugated iron loco sheds and an office with corrugated iron roof and interior wooden paneling. Visitors were to be taken from Hirwain station to the site of the sale and back by "the Contractor's train", which was to meet the 10.29am and 11.39am down Vale of Neath trains and return at 6pm and 7pm. The locomotives in this sale would be those surplus to Morrison and Mason's current further requirements and were:

*(clearly standard gauge):*
　　one 6-coupled ic 13in by Hunslet and one 6-coupled oc 14in by Avonside.

*(clearly 3ft gauge):*
　　two 4-coupled 6in cyls. by KS and one 4-coupled 6½in cyls. by KS, (presumably KS 644, 651 and 706 respectively); one 4-coupled 6½in cyls. by Andrew Barclay (probably No.5).

Earlier disposals have already been suggested in the text for most of the other narrow gauge locomotives.

*Morrison & Mason used an interesting fleet of 3ft gauge locos at Ystradfellte. Kerr Stuart 644 of 1899 appears to be a 'Sirdar' class but with a dropped footplate. Photographed on M&M''s Rhayader pipeline contract (Ludlow section) about 1902.* 　　　　　　　*[R W Miller Collection]*

# Chapter 5

## Penderyn: a modest project using two gauges for Mountain Ash Urban District Council

Just as Morrison and Mason were nearing the end of their work in the wilds of Ystradfellte, the building of a much smaller and more accessible reservoir, known as Penderyn (or alternatively Trebanog), was being started. The promoters were the Mountain Ash UDC whose territory lay over to the east; their contractor was William Underwood & Brother of Dukinfield, near Hyde, in Cheshire. Underwood was born in 1855 and died in 1924. With his stepbrother, G H Walker, he formed the partnership of Underwood & Brother in 1887. He was Mayor of Dukinfield three times, in 1909/10, 1911/12 and 1921/22.

The Mountain Ash Water Act of 1910 authorised the abstraction of water from the stream flowing through Bodwigiad Farm, the Nant-y-Deri, and also from the Nant-y-Bwllfa. The scheme involved gathering these waters and piping them to the reservoir at grid reference SN 938072. This reservoir was a purely artificial conception, with embankments to be constructed on three sides; only on the northern side does it abut on higher ground, and the surface water from this hillside was permanently diverted away from the reservoir. The deepest trench had to be dug near the southwest corner, after removal of poor rock. The usual construction was adopted - trench down to good rock, concrete in the trench, embankments built up of earth and a puddle-clay core seating on the concrete, all the embankments finished off with stone pitching on their water faces. The lake is shown on our map (page 57) about two miles north west of Hirwaun township and on ground just north of the Vale of Neath Railway but above it. As built, the top water level is 700ft above o.d. and the capacity 132 million gallons.

The contractor secured clay by digging a puddle field about a half-mile north of the site, on higher ground just short of the Rhigos - Penderyn hill road at about 950ft above o.d., and indeed with further digging of clay on the far side of this road. His silica stone quarry was beyond this by-road, roughly one third of a mile west of the puddle fields. He put in a 3ft gauge railway between quarry and clay fields, with access tracks to the clay field workings, and a self-acting incline down to the northern edge of the intended lake. The narrow gauge tracks also made a circuit of the lake area. A pug mill for the clay and crushers for stone were sited near the incline foot. A narrow gauge locomotive shed, a long one-road building, with adjoining fitters' and blacksmiths' shops and stores, was at the east end of the site, where the private road now approaches. Here was also exchange of traffic from a standard gauge line about three quarters of a mile long, which Underwood laid to connect (at grid reference SN 953073) with the Aberdare Canal Company's Hirwaun-Penderyn Quarry line. There was a siding at the junction with the latter near Lletty-Rhys farm, a bridge over the stream and a level crossing over the present A4059 road, from which the route to the site was along the approach road.

Underwood started work in 1911. There was not great activity on his standard gauge line. Such wagon loads as came in, for example coal, cement and pipes, were brought from the GWR station yard at Hirwaun by W. P. Powell's Penderyn Quarries locomotive as far as the siding near Lletty-Rhys, and thence hauled over the contractor's branch line by his small standard gauge locomotive:

*Contractor William Underwood (and chauffeur) in his Ford near the reservoir site. The steam road-roller is a Fowler compound of, perhaps, 1890s vintage.* [David Tipper Collection]

ARKAYAR    0-4-0 saddle tank    oc 11in x 16in

by Hudswell Clarke 303 of 1888. She was new to Robert K. Roberts (hence the strange compounded nameplate carried throughout her life) of Stormer End bleach works, Tottington in Lancashire. Underwood acquired the locomotive c.1911; she was usually driven by Walt Nicholas (ex the nearby Ystradfellte contract) here. In general, the traffic only demanded the lighting up of ARKAYAR on two or three days weekly. When not in use the engine stood in the open near the narrow gauge shed and the present reservoir keeper's house. A photograph at Penderyn shows Jack McGregor, fitter and driver, on the footplate. Subsequently Underwood sold her to the Partington Steel & Iron Co Ltd (later Lancashire Steel Corporation), Irlam Steelworks, Lancs.; she arrived there c.1917 - 1918, certainly by 8/1918. The company used her at their Bodfari casting-sand pits, Flintshire, from c.1924 until closure of the pits c.1934 and she was scrapped on site about 1939.

A Whittaker steam excavator dug into the northern hillside and the narrow gauge distributed this "muck" around to build up the embankments. Rough stone for protecting the lower slopes of the banks was secured when digging down to a rock foundation. Stone for pitching (facing the banks) was from the silica quarry. This and the puddle clay were brought down the incline in "runs" of four trucks on the rope, with empties ascending to provide partial balance. Dressed stone came in by rail on the standard gauge branch, as did cement for the concrete plant. Most similar projects came to a standstill around 1915 due to lack of labour but this one was on a modest scale and was carried on, albeit at a lethargic rate, during World War 1 by the employment of conscientious objectors to war service, who were quartered nearby and expected to undertake work of importance. The difficulties of this period brought varied work and promotion to Mr D Hughes, whose family lived at Penderyn and who joined Underwood on the job as a lad, cleaning the locomotives. He worked with the fitters and blacksmiths and soon progressed to driving a narrow gauge locomotive; and later also helped the one old boilermaker who remained on the staff.

*Underwood again (right) with his standard gauge loco ARKAYAR (Hudswell Clarke 303) and driver Jack McGregor. The photograph is believed to have been taken where the reservoir line crossed the the Hirwaun to Brecon Road (now the A4059).* [David Tipper Collection]

*Bagnall 1639 of 1901, of 3ft gauge, is said to have worked at Penderyn named INA, and previously had been with Morrison & Mason at Ystradfellte (Chapter.4). She was new as LIPSCOMB at Enoch Tempest's Walshaw Dean contract, W Yorks, where photographed.* [Frank Jones Collection]

*Bagnall 1669 of 1902,* DUKINFIELD, *one of the 3ft gauge fleet at Penderyn, was named after Underwood's home town in Cheshire. She later worked on Underwood's Grwyne Fawr contract (see Chapter 6). The dainty rolling stock used at Penderyn is worth examination.* [Aberdare Library]

Sometime during the war Underwood relinquished the contract and later the Mountain Ash UDC administered it direct. Probably Underwood's departure from Penderyn was about 1916-1917. The UDC commenced work in 1919 and the reservoir was brought into use in 1920. Much of the plant was moved around 1921, although some locomotives were still for sale in 1924. Underwood had another reservoir job in hand at Grwyne Fawr, in the Black Mountains near the Herefordshire border (see Chapter 6), and in 1916 he negotiated his release from that contract. (Labour for contractors was particularly scarce at this period of the war).

By April 1913 Underwood had moved at least one 3ft gauge locomotive (DUKINFIELD) from Penderyn to Grwyne Fawr and a steamroller was likewise transferred. The roller, a 6 tonner, had been used to drive the crusher at Penderyn and had an adventurous journey to Grwyne Fawr with a hare-brained driver. In bleak Dowlais, the domestic ash buckets had been put outside the terrace houses for collection that day and the roller, climbing the long, steep street, flattened them from end to end, pursued by a horde of yelling women. Later in the journey the roller collided with a doctor's trap on a humped-back bridge; it is said that the doctor was killed in the accident. Subsequently a Robey portable engine drove the Penderyn crusher.

The 3ft gauge locomotives at Penderyn comprised:

STANLEY   0-4-0 saddle tank   oc 8in x 14in
   by Black Hawthorn 872 of 1886. New as STANLEY to Heywood Corporation in Lancashire at Clay Lane Reservoir; later employed by contractor Enoch Tempest on Clough Bottom Reservoir, also in Lancs, built c.1889 - 1896. Underwood is believed to have had her by c.1900 on a filter bed construction contract in Lancs. She still carried her name on brass plates at Penderyn - and was said to be the first narrow gauge loco here. At first she worked down on the reservoir site, then later in the puddle field above the incline and on the puddle field to quarry section. She ran away down the incline and toppled over on one occasion. Driver Fred Aslett survived! She may have had a short spell away at Grwyne Fawr, but if so came back and is recalled staying to the end at Penderyn. She was at Grwyne Fawr again in Abertillery Water Board days but, if the above information from Penderyn is correct, she probably did not serve at Grwyne Fawr under the auspices of Underwood and was likely sold to the Board via A R Adams, Newport, in 6/1925.

CHOCOLATE (a nickname on account of her colour);
    This locomotive also had a number. Described as elderly, with cab propped on pillars, and thought to be by Kerr Stuart. It is just possible that one of the three Kerr Stuarts used by Morrison and Mason at Ystradfellte (referred to in the preceding chapter) was hired by Underwood before the locomotives were sold in 5/1915, although they could not be called elderly.

INA    0-4-0 saddle tank.
    Thought to be probably by W G Bagnall and named by Underwood after a daughter or grand-daughter. Stated to have been brought by Underwood from the north of England (but see below); still on site in about 1921, after completion of the job. Her probable identity is WB 1639 of 1901 (oc 8in x 12in) - new to Enoch Tempest on the Walshaw Dean Reservoir project for Halifax Corporation (see *Yorkshire Pennines*) as LIPSCOMB and then with Morrison and Mason Ltd at Ystradfellte. The presence of WB 1639 at Penderyn is supported by the supply of spares in 1919. Later with M & M again at Lower Laithe Reservoir, W. Yorks, and passed to Sir William Arrol & Co Ltd in 1921, (see *Bowland Forest & Craven Country*). Sold in 6/1925 to John Best & Sons Ltd and on to Richard Baillie at Hopes Reservoir, East Lothian, c.1931 and Ladybower Reservoir, Derbys, from 1935. But note that spares were also booked to Mountain Ash UDC, Penderyn, for WB 1683 of 1902 (originally Tempest's ANNIE and later at Manchester Corporation's Heaton Park Reservoir project).

*This good-looking six-coupled saddletank, WEST BALDWIN, was Hunslet 758 of 1901 and named after a reservoir in the Isle of Man. After leaving Penderyn she worked at the Harbury Cement Works, Warwicks, of Greaves, Bull & Lakin where this photograph was probably taken in the early 1920s.*
*[Frank Jones Collection]*

*This close-up of* DUKINFIELD *shows the troublesome flangeless centre driving wheels and Underwood's owner's plate on the cab side. Fred Aslett is the driver, Bill Spiller his colleague on the left.* [H D Bowtell Collection]

WEST BALDWIN   0-6-0 saddle tank   oc 9in x 14in.
   by Hunslet 758 of 1901. Had been new with Douglas Corporation building West Baldwin Reservoir in the Isle of Man; there repainted 12/1905, and c.1/1907 acquired by Preston Corporation and used on the enlargement of their Spade Mill N°.1 Reservoir, Lancs, a job of 1907 - 1910 (see *Bowland Forest & Craven Country*). She had bold brass nameplates and was recalled as of attractive appearance - but is said to have been broken up at Penderyn before the end of the job, only the whistle being kept. However, Hunslet records have the locomotive with J F Wake, the Darlington dealer, in 5/1918 and thereafter (by 6/1920) with Greaves, Bull & Lakin at Harbury Cement Works, Warwicks, where she was scrapped in 1926.

DUKINFIELD (with No.4 on her bunker) 0-6-0 saddle tank   oc 9in x 14in
   by W G Bagnall 1669 of 1902. Had been new to Enoch Tempest on his Walshaw Dean Reservoir job, his TENACITY.  The property of Underwood by 5/1912, he subsequently named her DUKINFIELD.  She had flangeless driving wheels at Penderyn (and they gave trouble); the flangeless wheels appear in a photograph there, with Bill Spiller on the ground and Fred Aslett, driver, on the footplate. It is recalled that she was sent to Underwood's Grwyne Fawr job and there is evidence to suggest that she was there as early as 6/1913 (by 4/1913 according to IRS).  She stayed there during the war, being used briefly by the Canadian Forestry Corps on timber cutting in the spring of 1917, and worked on to completion afterwards. DUKINFIELD was sold from there in 1928 by Abertillery Water Board to Lehane, Mackenzie and Shand - used by them at Gorple Reservoirs contract, West Yorks (for Halifax Corporation, see *Yorkshire Pennines*) as BURTON. She was later at Lehane's Darley Dale yard.  Photographs of DUKINFIELD at Penderyn show a rectangular owner's plate on the left-hand cab side whereas a wartime photograph at Grwyne Fawr shows a small oval Bagnall plate on the right-hand cab side.

MOUNTAIN ASH   0-4-0 saddle tank   oc 9in x 14in

by W. G. Bagnall 1682 of 1902. Had been new with Tempest at Walshaw Dean as GEORGE. Illustrated at Penderyn with the painted name MOUNTAIN ASH, also with "44" painted on her cab upper panel and sporting a spark-arresting chimney. The number suggests employment prior to Penderyn by a concern with many locos but no intervening owner has been identified.   The locomotive was first used on the top level, from the quarry and puddle field to the incline head. An irregular evening escapade up the hilly line towards the quarry ended in the loco running back and going through the end of her shed, the driver being "sacked". Probably sold in 1924 - 1925 to A R Adams, along with STANLEY, and thence to the Abertillery Board at Grwyne Fawr, who acquired her in mid 1925.  Later again - via Joseph Pugsley, the Bristol dealer, to Derby Corporation's direct labour land reclamation scheme at Derby Riverlands, 1932-1934, where named DORA, and for a time RIVERLANDS DORA (see *Manchester & the Peak*). She was finally sold to H Potter & Co, dealers of Nottingham.

*Bagnall 1682 of 1902,* MOUNTAIN ASH, *seen at Penderyn with her spark-arresting chimney. Fred Aslett is again the driver on the cab; the others from the left are "Bristol Gypsy", Tommy Luker and Jim Dunn. How this loco came to carry the number '44' is a mystery; she later worked at Grwyne Fawr.*

*[Richard Evans Collection]*

XIT   0-4-0 saddle tank   oc 8in x 14in.

by Manning Wardle 475 of 1874. For the early history of this locomotive and the origin of her name see under Upper Neuadd Reservoir in Chapter 3. After Upper Neuadd, Holme and King of Liverpool used her on the LYR widening scheme at Brighouse, W Yorks, at Liverpool Waterworks' Prescot Reservoir, Lancs, and at Bradford Corporation's Angram Reservoir (see *Yorkshire Dales*). Later still they used her on two jobs at Coventry: building Courtaulds' factory and the Coventry Loop Line for the LNWR. XIT became LNWR property when H & K went into liquidation and was offered for sale by them at Gosford Green, Coventry, on 23/7/1914. Presumably then purchased by Underwood, she is recalled arriving at Penderyn after the war had started. She is said to have left Penderyn before the finish of the job but has not been traced in any later sphere.  It is suggested she may have been requisitioned by the MoM. This charming little engine was variously known at Penderyn as "Exit" or "Exits"!

It will be seen from the foregoing that WEST BALDWIN, DUKINFIELD and XIT did not remain at Penderyn into the UDC era in 1919. The engines offered for sale from the Penderyn site as late as 7/2/1924 (*Machinery Market*, 18/1/1924) were merely described as "four 3ft gauge locomotives". Perhaps these would be STANLEY and MOUNTAIN ASH - sold to A R Adams and thence to the Abertillery Board at Grwyne Fawr; and the mysterious CHOCOLATE and INA  - sold for further service; (WB 1639 was later with Morrison & Mason at Keighley Corporation's Lower Laithe Reservoir project, West Yorks). By this time the little reservoir at Penderyn would be merging into the landscape.

# Notes on Earlier Mountain Ash Projects

Prior to the construction of Penderyn reservoir, the Mountain Ash local authorities had built two small reservoirs that soon proved inadequate for the rapidly growing population of the district, which was to peak in the early 1920s. Further information on these two early projects would be most welcome.

## *Clydach Reservoir, Llanwonno*

Clydach Reservoir was constructed, by an as-yet-unknown contractor, for the Mountain Ash Local Board of Health. The reservoir, of 12 million gallons capacity, was built 1889-1893 at a cost of "over £2,000". It is at grid reference ST 028967 on the Nant Clydach stream beyond the Llanwonno terminus of the TVR Clydach Valley branch, opened c.1884 and closed beyond Mynachdy Colliery loop in 1931. No definite information on the use of railways or locomotives at this site is available, but Henry Parker, a machinery dealer and/or contractor, advertised in *The Engineer*, 17/1/1890, from Bryn Clydach, Ynysybwl, for six locos, 3ft gauge, not under 10inch.

## *Perthgelyn Reservoir*

The 31 million gallon Perthgelyn Reservoir (at grid reference ST 053970) is on the hillside between the Cynon and Clydach (Ynysybwl) valleys. The contractor was Thomas Taylor of Pontypridd, who later moved into colliery ownership sinking the Nantgarw pit from 1910. Work on the reservoir, built under the Mountain Ash Water & Gas Act of 1900, started in 1902 and connection of the new supply to houses in Mountain Ash, Penrhiwceiber and Abercynon was largely complete by October 1903. Taylor brought materials to a point near Cwm Crossing on the TVR Clydach Valley branch above Ynysybwl. Having failed to agree terms with the Taff Vale Railway for the installation of a dedicated siding at Cwm, Taylor got permission to unload directly off the very lightly used 'main line' onto a timber loading stage from which a narrow gauge line ran roughly north-east for about half a mile to the reservoir site. No additional information on Taylor's narrow gauge line has yet come to light.

# Chapter 6

## The Abertillery & District Water Board
## in the Grwyne Fawr Valley

The Abertillery & District Water Board was constituted by an Act of Parliament that received the Royal Assent on 3 August 1910. It was a consortium formed by the Abertillery, Abercarn, Risca and Mynyddislwyn Urban District Councils. The 1910 Act provided for the new board to construct a reservoir to obviate the difficulties with the earlier Cwmtillery Reservoir (see the notes at the end of this chapter) and to supply the still growing population of the area. The project involved an exciting scheme - eventually achieved by the Board - for a 400 million gallon reservoir with a top water level of 1,790ft above o.d., in the Black Mountains on the borders of the pre-1974 counties of Brecknock, Hereford and Monmouth. The lake and most of the works were just inside the first named county. The site of the dam is shown on 1: 50 000 first series OS map sheet 161 (Abergavenny & the Black Mountains) at grid reference SO 233307, about one mile north east of the Pen-y-Manllwyn-Waunfach ridge, which, at 2,500ft, commands magnificent westward views to the Beacons and over Radnorshire.

Apart from the dam at Grwyne Fawr, other notable features of the scheme were 33 miles of pipeline, including a tunnel through Coity Mountain and two two-million-gallon service reservoirs at Cwmtillery (at grid reference SO 223076, near the earlier Abertillery UDC reservoir) and above Aberbeeg (the "Abercarn tank" at grid reference SO 199015). The pipeline was thus to serve the domestic water needs of the four local authorities. Rather surprisingly for the period, the initial plan was to access the remote dam site by a newly constructed ten-mile-long road. William Underwood & Brother's tender of £261,745 was accepted by the Board in December 1911; one source (*Building News*) named the contractors as Underwood & Walker — G H Walker was Underwood's stepbrother. The first sod for the new road was cut on 14 February 1912 and the first sod for the reservoir on 16 October of the same year by Councillor David Lewis, Vice Chairman of the Water Board. A silver cup commemorating the latter event still survives.

Mr Baldwin Latham of Westminster had been appointed the Board's Consultant Engineer and his son J D Latham took on the role of Resident Engineer. John Francis Jupp, whom we shall later encounter in connection with Newport Corporation's Talybont project, was the Board's surveyor on the job. The Manager of Works was Abram Messam. Construction of the dam, across a narrow steep sided and wild valley, was in concrete, with a near vertical downstream face, 156ft high, stone faced, with overflow water running down it from a colonnade immediately below the top walkway. A large quarry for stone was opened up at the far end of the reservoir site, where only the upper part of its face shows today above high water. Cement and other materials had to come from the world outside these mountains. Work began in 1912 by laying a pipeline and building a narrow road atop it up the valley. For a time horses and traction engines struggled over the eleven or twelve miles from the GWR's Llanvihangel station, but the difficulties involved led Underwood, in November 1912, to request the Board to allow him to put down a light railway along the new road. Llanvihangel station, itself 500ft above o.d., is known to train timers as the summit on the GWR between Hereford and Abergavenny, Thence from Llanfihangel (note the generally accepted spelling of the village) to the foot of the dam the waterworks traffic had to climb some 1,140ft - not to mention occasional dips in the road. The 3ft gauge adhesion-worked railway that followed eventually reached fully 1,790ft at the top of the dam, nearly 1,300ft above the station, making it the most consistently severe of our British waterworks lines and almost certainly the highest at the summit.

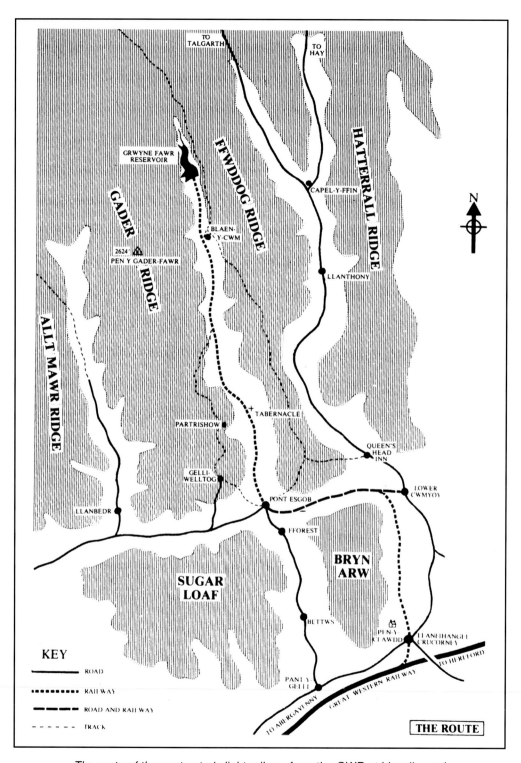

*The route of the contractor's light railway from the GWR at Llanvihangel
Station to the reservoir construction site at Grwyne Fawr*

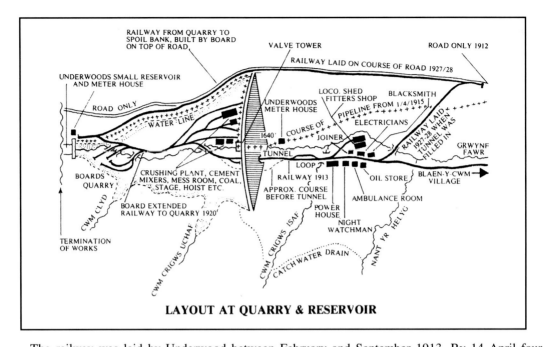

**LAYOUT AT QUARRY & RESERVOIR**

The railway was laid by Underwood between February and September 1913. By 14 April four miles had been laid from Lower Cwmyoy, just off the B4423 Llanfihangel-Llanthony road below Llwyncelyn farm, up the valley. Three locomotives and 160 wagons had arrived on the line. The remaining six miles to the foot of the proposed dam was complete at 17 September. The ten-mile route was on the new private road (built as part of the reservoir scheme for Lord Glanusk and other landlords whose estates it crossed), leaving room for road vehicles to pass only at regular passing places. Rail of 50 to 75 pounds per yard was used and the steepest gradient was 1 in 9 for 150 yards. Underwood tried but failed to negotiate a railway right of way on from Cwmyoy to Llanvihangel station yard, so was forced to continue using road haulage from Lower Cwmyoy to the station yard, about one and a half miles. The contractor's focal points of activity in the years 1913-1916 were thus Llanvihangel station yard, Lower Cwmyoy (with transhipment and a loco shed), Blaen-y-Cwm (also with a loco shed) and a site on the valley floor near the dam construction (with workshops). Blaen-y-Cwm was about two miles below the construction site and here a hutted village was built in 1913-1914 on both sides of the road and railway and close beside the stream. It included various types of living quarters, a mission hall, canteen, school (opened May 1914) and small hospital (1915). The line later also went beyond the dam site up the floor of the valley to a quarry.

Underwood clearly found the work on the dam foundations and on the pipe tunnel, concurrent with his activity at Penderyn, to be onerous and a strain on his resources. Progress was slow; soon came the war and he gave up the contract in December 1916, although the pipeline including the Coity Mountain tunnel had been completed by April 1915. Four miles of track at the top end of the valley were lifted on the orders of the Ministry of Munitions but in the spring of 1917 fifteen men of the Canadian Forestry Corps were installed for a month, using locomotive DUKINFIELD to haul timber down the valley to Lower Cwmyoy. In 1919, with the peace, the Water Board set to work to carry through the project by direct labour. They had purchased Underwood's plant and equipment, including two locomotives, at Blaen-y-Cwm for £30,000 on 1 December 1916 when they took over the works from the contractor and now acquired another locomotive from war surplus stocks. A route across fields from Lower Cwmyoy to Llanvihangel station yard was negotiated and the railway was then

*A fine shot of the dam site showing the tunnel through which the quarry was accessed. It was later filled in and a zig-zag line built to take the railway past the dam above top dam height. ANITA at centre and one of the large Manning Wardles at left.*

*[ © Abergavenny Museum, Monmouthshire County Council]*

*Beyond the dam heading towards the quarry, at about 1,790 feet above sea level at the summit point of the line, is DUKINFIELD. This was the highest level reached by any adhesion worked railway in the British Isles. Note the 'Blondin' aerial ropeway in use.*

*[ © Abergavenny Museum, Monmouthshire County Council]*

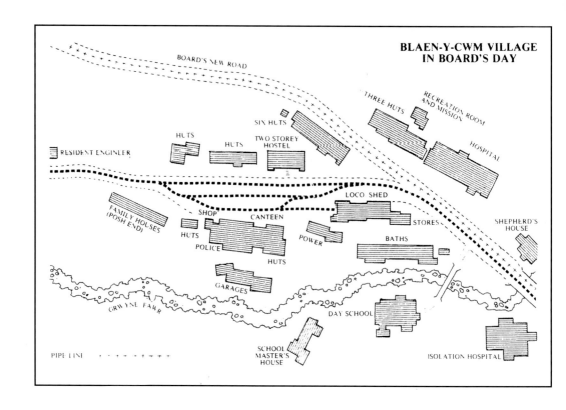

BLAEN-Y-CWM VILLAGE
IN BOARD'S DAY

BOARD'S NEW ROAD

RESIDENT ENGINEER

HUTS

SIX HUTS

HUTS

TWO STOREY HOSTEL

THREE HUTS

RECREATION ROOM AND MISSION

HOSPITAL

FAMILY HOUSES (POSH END)

SHOP

CANTEEN

LOCO SHED

STORES

SHEPHERD'S HOUSE

HUTS

POLICE

POWER

BATHS

HUTS

GARAGES

GRWYNE FAWR

DAY SCHOOL

PIPE LINE

SCHOOL MASTER'S HOUSE

ISOLATION HOSPITAL

*The dam at Grwyne Fawr on 29 March 1978, with water overflowing the top.*     *[Harold D Bowtell]*

76

extended, thus providing direct exchange with the GWR siding. The Cwmyoy locomotive shed was replaced by one at Llanfihangel.

The years immediately after World War I were difficult ones and, like most waterworks projects, this one made slow progress until about 1925, when additional locomotives were obtained and work pushed forward to completion, with inauguration on 29 March 1928. Councillor Lewis again officiated and this time was rewarded with a golden key. A "tunnel" through the dam to accommodate the line on to the quarry was retained until a late stage, believed September 1927.

At that time, or earlier, a steep zigzag route was built from near the dam workshops to reach the dam top level on the northern side of the valley and this line is said to have continued as far as the quarry. This new line crossed the 1,800ft contour, the highest altitude reached by an adhesion worked railway in the British Isles. The locomotives were all sold for further service in 1928-1929 and the railway was dismantled in 1929. Today the Forestry Commission is the main tenant of the valley up to Blen-y-Cwm, where a picnic site uses the foundations of the village. Beyond here is as wild as before 1912, fine walking country.

*The view downstream from Grwyne Fawr dam on 29/3/1978. The cars are parked in the area of Blaen-y-Cwm loco shed and workshops. The steep course of the 3ft gauge up the embankment can be seen and continued, via reversal, to the top of the dam and a quarry at c.1790ft.*     *[H D Bowtell]*

This account of a mountainous line has been kept brief, as the late Rev David Tipper enthusiastically made it his speciality and has spoken and written at length upon it, notably in two editions of *Stone and Steam in the Black Mountains* (published privately in 1975, and by Blorenge Books in 1985). Cooperation with Mr Tipper was a pleasure and access to his findings is acknowledged with appreciation. Details of locomotives, all 3ft gauge, follow –

ANITA    0-4-0 saddle tank    oc 9½in x 14in

by Manning Wardle 1630 of 1904. Originally owned by Elliott's Metal Company, Burry Port, Carms, being their ANITA. It had a low footplate to the cab and carried nameplates at Grwyne Fawr. In use here by Underwood by 1913 (local information). Quoted as a strong engine, taking eight tons of cement up the valley. Remained based at Blaen-y-Cwm during the 1914-1918 war and passed to the Water Board in 12/1916. In 1923 it was the regular engine for the "Paddy Mails". Driven by Harry Bayliss Snr, Bill Kirby and Jack O'Hearne when with the Board. Sold in 6/1928 to contractors Lehane, Mackenzie and Shand Ltd, becoming their DERBY, and used on their Brownhill Reservoir contract, Holmbridge, Yorks (there 5/1930), their Gorple Reservoirs job of 1927-1934 for Halifax Corporation (see *Yorkshire Pennines*); later at their Fernilee Reservoir contract, Derbyshire, c.1933-1937, for Stockport Corporation, (see *Manchester & the Peak*) then to Lehane's Darley Dale yard. In use at Bovis's Hapton, Lancs, contract c.1940, and subsequently with Paulings building the Magnesium Elektron factory at Burnley, Lancs, 1942-1943, for the Ministry of Supply. Subsequently at Paulings' Crymlyn Burrows depot, Swansea, where broken up c.1951.

DUKINFIELD    0-6-0 saddle tank    oc 9in x 14in

by W.G. Bagnall 1669 of 1902. Its earlier history is recorded (Chapter 5) under Penderyn, whence it came c.1913. It was working here by 25/6/1913 (being off the road and overturned that day). Retained at Blaen-y-Cwm during World War I and passed to the Water Board in 12/1916. As described in the text this loco was briefly used for timber haulage by the Canadian Forestry Corps during the War after work on the reservoir ceased. This is the loco that displayed an oblong (owners) plate on the left hand cab side in a picture at Penderyn but a small oval one on the right hand side at Grwyne Fawr. It was sometimes called ABERTILLERY No. 3. In 1923 it was normally kept at the dam site but worked the "Mails" when ANITA was out of service. Driven by Joe Williams, Harry Bayliss Snr and Charlie Rawlings when with the Board. Sold in 6/1928 direct to Lehane, Mackenzie and Shand, becoming their BURTON at Gorple Reservoirs (see *Yorkshire Pennines*); possibly later at Fernilee and definitely at Lehane's Darley Dale yard in 11/1937. No subsequent record.

*Manning Wardle 1630 of 1904* ANITA *was a 'special' design. Bill Kirby is the driver, Joe Weaver obscures the name. Note the 'legs of Man' on the cab sheet.*
*[ © Abergavenny Museum, Monmouthshire County Council]*

DUKINFIELD *is an old friend illustrated at Penderyn (Chapter 5) and with* ANITA *was definitely brought here by Underwood in 1913 and stayed on to be later used by the Board.*

[ © *Abergavenny Museum, Monmouthshire County Council]*

BRIGG    0-4-0 saddle tank    oc 9in x 15in
> by Hudswell Clarke 504 of 1899. New to Newcastle and Gateshead Water Company on their direct labour job building Catcleugh Reservoir, Northumberland, c.1898-1905 (see *Durham's Dales to the Borders*); with Manchester contractor George Bell (via the makers), c.7/1905, and possibly used on his Chatsworth estate contract, Derbys, 7/1905- 9/1909; by 12/2/1912 and via J. Wardell & Co., dealers, London, with Harold Arnold at his Leighton Reservoir job in Colsterdale (see *Yorkshire Dales*); then drifted into wartime duties. Acquired by the Abertillery Water Board from the Ministry of Munitions at Barnbow in 1919; the decision to purchase was minuted 30 June 1919 at a time of difficulty as DUKINFIELD was reported broken down (note the name DUKINFIELD then still in use); BRIGG had arrived by 9/1919. Kept at the dam site in 1919. Recollections are of a snowplough attached in winter. Driven by Harry Bayliss Snr and Bill Pattimore. Sold direct in 5/1928 to Lehane, Mackenzie and Shand, their HESWALL at Gorple (see *Yorkshire Pennines*) and Fernilee (Goyt Valley, see *Manchester & the Peak*) Reservoirs, and in Darley Dale yard in 1939. Finally with William Twigg, the Matlock dealer, who scrapped her after WW2.

STANLEY   0-4-0 saddle tank    oc 8in x 14in
> by Black Hawthorn 872 of 1886. Earlier history is recorded (Ch 5) under Penderyn, there the property of Underwood; he may have moved the loco to Grwyne Fawr but if so it returned to Penderyn, probably in 1916, as Underwood was then reported to have moved two locos from Grwyne Fawr. It was definitely at Grwyne Fawr during the Board's regime, presumably sold by the Mountain Ash UDC (Penderyn) to A R Adams, the Newport dealer, in 1924-1925 and acquired from Adams by the Abertillery Board in 6/1925, arriving 7/1925. Driven by Arthur Ridout in the Board's ownership. Sold in 12/1928 from Grwyne Fawr to Joseph Pugsley and Son, dealers, of Bristol. No further trace.

BRIGG *was Hudswell Clarke 504 of 1898 and arrived after the end of World War I in Water Board days. Bill Pattimore is the driver.* [ © Abergavenny Museum, Monmouthshire County Council]

STANLEY *(Black Hawthorn 872 of 1886) may have worked at Grwyne Fawr under both regimes, and is seen here with driver Arthur Ridout.* [ © Abergavenny Museum, Monmouthshire County Council]

*The Rev. Hughes of St Michael's, Llanfihangel and his sister grace a workman's coach coupled to*
ABERTILLERY N°.1 *beside the Llanfihangel loco shed, 1922.*
*[ © Abergavenny Museum, Monmouthshire County Council]*

ABERTILLERY N°.2 *(Manning Wardle 1986 of 1920) was the second of two large engines bought*
*new by the Water Board. Though imposing looking, their early days of use were not without*
*problems.* *[ © Abergavenny Museum, Monmouthshire County Council]*

MOUNTAIN ASH   0-4-0 saddle tank   oc 9in x 14in
   by W. G. Bagnall 1682 of 1902. Earlier history is recorded (Ch 5) under Penderyn. It was
   Underwood's property at Penderyn and later came to Grwyne Fawr - but this was probably in the
   Water Board's time; like STANLEY it would be one of the two engines reported arriving at Grwyne
   Fawr from Adams in 6 or 7/1925. Sold from Grwyne Fawr 12/1928 to Joseph Pugsley of Bristol,
   thence to Derby Corporation's Derby Riverlands project, 1932-1934, as DORA (and at one period
   RIVERLANDS DORA). To H Potter & Co, the Nottingham dealer, in 1934. No further trace.

ABERTILLERY N°.1   0-6-0 saddle tank   oc 11in x 17in
   by Manning Wardle 1985 of 1920. Came new, arriving at Llanvihangel station on 29/4/1920.
   Stabled at Llanfihangel and worked traffic over the "route" (main line) up the valley to Blaen-y-Cwm.
   Driven by Billy Hoffland (with Dai Lewis as fireman /rope runner) and later by Mr Holland. For
   disposal - see the following text.

ABERTILLERY N°.2   0-6-0 saddle tank   oc 11in x 17in
   by Manning Wardle 1986 of 1920 - arrived new on 6/5/1920. Stationed at Blaen-y-cwm and (inter
   alia) worked a "Mail" down the valley on Saturdays with shoppers for GWR trains. Driven by Bill
   Perrin, Mr Wiseman and Bill Kirby. Used on track lifting in 1928-1929, the last loco in steam. For
   disposal - see the following text.

These last two locomotives were remarkably large for the job and with their lengthy overhang were not
trouble free on the line. They "bounced" alarmingly on the light track and both were out of action with
damaged springs within a month of arriving. Mannings sent a man to the site to examine the problems;
the rear springs were changed, compensating beams were fitted to all springs and a five cwt. block of
lead was bolted to the front end of both locos. The last spares for them were ordered in February 1929.
Joseph Pugsley, the Bristol dealer and scrap merchant, paid £3,300 for four locomotives (STANLEY,
MOUNTAIN ASH and ABERTILLERY N°.1 and N°.2), the track, a concrete hoist and some scrap metal.

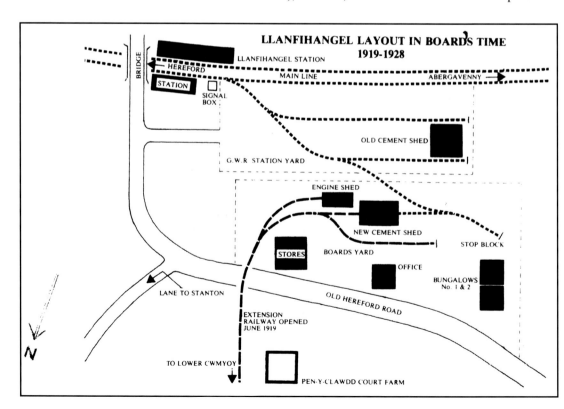

*An idyllic setting at Blaen-y-Cwm in the Black Mountains, complete with narrow gauge railway to the Grwyne Fawr reservoir construction site.   [© Abergavenny Museum, Monmouthshire County Council]*

All seven 3ft gauge steam locomotives were offered for sale by the Water Board in an announcement of 5 October 1927 (*Contract Journal*), with two remaining for disposal at 25 July 1928. At least one locomotive during the Underwood period appears unaccounted for as Water Board minutes implied that he had four locomotives "in the district". It was recorded that in May 1916 he was allowed by the Board to sell two locomotives for £320, one of them being used on "one of the service reservoirs". HDB has taken it that the other one was **STANLEY**, disposed of (to Penderyn) in 1916, but Rev Tipper discounts HDB's theory concerning **STANLEY** doing two spells of duty on the line, firstly with Underwood and then with the Water Board in the direct labour era.

By September 1929 the two large Mannings were in the Avonside Engine Company's works in Bristol for overhaul under arrangements in which Pugsley and dealer George Cohen participated. They were consigned from Bristol on 19 October 1929, bound for the Municipality of Singapore where they worked on a reservoir project bringing water supply to the "Lion City". In March 1932 two new boilers were ordered from Kitsons, by then successors to Manning Wardle. By 1934 they are said to have been observed at Kowloon, Hong Kong, on some unspecified project.

As we have seen there were two service reservoirs, at Cwmtillery and above Aberbeeg, on the pipeline from Grwyne Fawr. One (but which?) is known to have been served by a narrow gauge tramway until its completion in 1915. It is of great interest that some years ago the Rev Tipper located a photograph in the possession of a Mr Lewis of Pont Esgob showing the dam site in the early (foundation laying) days, c.1915. The photo shows an apparent 0-4-2 side tank with outside cylinders and a "hole in the wall" tank and carrying nameplates that seem to read **GRWYNE FAWR**. This would be an Underwood engine at this date. Could this have been the locomotive used (earlier?) at the service

83

reservoir? Or indeed, the third loco referred to in April 1913? Unfortunately the present whereabouts of this photograph are not known. The three locomotives in the Grwyne Fawr valley in April 1913, in Underwood's time, would be ANITA, DUKINFIELD and possibly either STANLEY or the locomotive in the photograph described in this paragraph.

The railway boasted other interesting items of rolling stock apart from the locomotives. There was the 'glass coach', a saloon normally reserved for lady passengers only. This is thought to have been built by Kerr, Stuart & Co., c.1900 and acquired by the Water Board early in 1920. Originally open sided, it was fitted with glass windows at Grywne Fawr and featured in a number of illustrations of the line. It was sold to Lehane, Mackenzie & Shand in 1928 for use at Gorple reservoir and later passed to Boden's Stone Co Ltd at Stanton-in-the-Peak, Derbyshire, where it found use as a store. In 1957 it went to the Tal-y-llyn Railway Preservation Society where it became known as the 'Stanton coach'. The superstructure was badly decayed but the frame and running gear were used together with a new body to form carriage N°.16, which still finds use on the line.

An ambulance coach was also provided, probably in 1922, solely to evacuate badly injured men from the remote site. Mercifully it was seldom used. A stretcher was slung from the roof by hooks when the coach was in motion. This coach also boasted glazed windows unlike the fifteen (or so) four-wheeled coaches that were used on the workmen's mail trains. The body of the ambulance coach still survived in 1985 at Pen-y-Clawdd Court farm at Llanfihangel.

## Earlier Projects in the Water Board's Area

### *Abertillery New Waterworks Contract (Cwmtillery)*

A little-known firm of contractors, Bagley & Company, completed an earlier scheme, the "New Waterworks Contract, Abertillery" for Abertillery Urban District Council in about May 1897. This almost certainly comprised the construction of the 40 million gallon Cwmtillery Reservoir at grid reference SO 220071. The reservoir was authorised by an Act of 1894 and the intention was to daily provide 300,000 gallons to Lancaster's Steam Coal Collieries Ltd and 400,000 gallons for domestic use. Lancaster's mining operations caused subsidence and chronic leakage of reservoir water very soon after opening and within a few years the UDC was required to seek other sources of supply. Bagley's completion sale advertised in the *Western Mail* of 13/5/1897 included a Manning Wardle six-coupled locomotive with 11in by 17in cylinders, probably one of the makers' "Old I" class engines. No further details are available.

### *Nant-y-Draenog Reservoir*

This small reservoir was built c.1900 without any official authority by The Western Valleys Gas & Water Board. It is situated 700ft above o.d. at grid reference ST 189935 close to Mynyddislwyn village. It served the needs of the Risca area. From 1915 the Abertillery & District Water Board's pipeline from Grwyne Fawr via Coity Tunnel and the two service reservoirs terminated at Nant-y-Draenog Reservoir, 33 miles from Grwyne Fawr. The pipeline at this extremity thus served to top up the reservoir. Nothing is known of the contractor on this project or of the use of railways during construction. Nant-y-Draenog Reservoir only became redundant in 1979 following the development of Llandegfedd Reservoir (see Chapter 2). No information about the contractor at the site or the use of railways is available.

The three reservoirs discussed in this chapter will all have come under the control of the Gwent Water Board from 1 April 1970.

# Chapter 7

# The Corporation of Newport's Protracted Schemes at Wentwood and Talybont-on-Usk

Earlier we have seen that Cardiff Corporation's relations with their contractors demonstrated a theme of litigation, often in connection with work that had to be abandoned during time of war. Newport's reservoir projects on the other hand, as we shall see, can be characterised by inordinate delay and procrastination.

Newport & Pillgwenlly Water Works Company, with a capital of £20,000, was sanctioned in July 1846. Earlier in October 1845 an organising committee of leading citizens had appointed the distinguished water engineer James Simpson to prepare plans for a reservoir at Ynysyfro, at grid reference ST 282891. The reservoir, initially holding 70 million gallons and with a dam 42ft high, was opened in 1848 and enlarged in 1856. Following complaints about the discolouration of the water after heavy rains, the company decided to build another reservoir just above the original one. This became known as the 'subsiding reservoir' since, in addition to providing additional storage, it trapped silt coming down in time of flood. It was constructed by Thomas Docwra & Sons of London in c.1882 at a cost of £13,345; thus the two Ynysyfro reservoirs together came to hold 120 million gallons.

The company also developed Pant-yr-Eos Reservoir (145 million gallons), at grid reference ST 255915, which was built in 1874-1878 by Jonathan E Billups, the well-known Cardiff contractor. In 1926 the filter house at Pant-yr-Eos was greatly extended. Photographs show new filters being brought up to the reservoir on trailers by two steam road tractors and then floated on pontoons across the water to the installation site. Both of the steam engines were owned by the well-known Newport firm of Robert Wynn Limited, heavy haulage contractors. Unfortunately no information has as yet come to light concerning the use of railways at either Ynysyfro or Pant-yr-Eos reservoirs.

*New filters being delivered to Pant-yr-Eos by Robert Wynn & Sons Ltd of Newport, 1926. On right is Burrell G/M tractor 2842 of 1906 (AX 183) and the tractor on left is Wallis & Steevens compound 2846 of 1905 (AA 2037).* *[Newport City Libraries]*

**Above:** *The opening ceremony at Talybont reservoir on 29/6/1939. Alderman John Wardell the Mayor of Newport (second left) performs the ceremony in the valve tower watched by Major Wilfred Marsden the site engineer (centre) and the contractor John McColville (fourth left).* [Dwr Cymru Welsh Water]

**Below:** *Having completed the ceremony, the Mayor, civic dignitaries and invited guests all stroll back across the now opened dam.* [Dwr Cymru Welsh Water]

# Wentwood

The water company's name was changed in 1887 to Newport Waterworks Company and it was taken over by Newport Corporation in September 1888 at a cost of £287,000. The Corporation thus inherited reservoirs at two locations and also powers under the Newport Waterworks Act, 1887, including authority to build Llanvaches storage reservoir, which later came to be known as Wentwood Reservoir. Additional Corporation Acts of 1892 and 1897 (extension of time) were to follow. The Chairman of the Newport Waterworks Committee from its inception until 1902 was Alderman Charles Lyne, after whom one of the locomotives used on the construction project was to be named.

The Wentwood site is eight miles north east of the centre of Newport, on the southern fringe of the wooded Wentwood uplands, which rise to some 900ft. The dam is at grid reference ST 430929. The Engineer at the start of the project was Mr Conyers Kirby, who had been Borough Engineer at Newport, and his intention was to have an earth embankment constructed, with a puddle clay core and with the trench below ground level, down to rock, likewise filled with puddle clay, rather than concrete.

In August 1894, the contract for the works was let to James Young, quite a well-known contractor in Glasgow, and indeed in Scotland generally, at that time. His was the third lowest of fifteen bids and he was preferred over some illustrious names, including John Aird & Son and J T Firbank. The works were soon commenced but within about a year the contractor was thoroughly disturbed by his findings during excavation of the trench across the valley; it did not promise a good foundation and it was clear that his contract price of £94,596 would be inadequate. Accordingly, Young negotiated with the Corporation and was relieved of his contract by an agreement minuted 30 November 1895.

The Corporation of Newport took specialist advice and decided to resume construction but taking the cut-off trench down much deeper than originally envisaged, to some 120ft below the ground, in order to reach better rock, also filling the trench with concrete up to about ground level and puddle clay for the core of the dam above the ground. The prospective cost was increased and the works were to be executed by direct labour. In 1897 Conyers Kirby resigned and Mr Baldwin Latham, well known at this period, undertook the responsibilities of Engineer. The Corporation's Waterworks Manager was Mr C Cullum and the Works Manager at the site was James Macdonald, who was appointed in June 1896 and came from the employ of Failsworth UDC, near Manchester.

James Young seems to have established his depot near the limestone quarry that was opened out. This is believed to be the considerable quarry, now disused, which can be seen on the west side of the road, which runs northwards from Llanvaches village. The location is just short of the approach drive to the site. The quarry eventually provided stone for crushing, carried out at or near the quarry, in order to make concrete. Subsequently, stone for the protective pitching on the embankment's water face was obtained here.

Young planned to employ 3ft gauge site railways and rented land for this purpose at £2 6s per annum from landowner Evan Roberts. He is known to have laid his tramway in part of the road and also over a level crossing - which would be necessary to connect the quarry (and presumably the depot, too) with the site of the cut-off trench and eventual embankment. One steam locomotive was to be introduced on this tramway and another was ordered by the contractor. Concerning the identities of these, more anon. The first locomotive, along with Young's other plant, was taken over by the Corporation in November 1895, but correspondence indicates that it actually arrived at Wentwood soon after Young's departure. The second locomotive arrived around April 1896 from its maker, none other than Dugald Drummond, who had made a name as Locomotive Superintendent of the North British Railway (1875-1882) and the Caledonian Railway (1883-1890) and was later to have a lengthy

*Wentwood reservoir under construction with the trench being filled with puddle clay.  Two tip wagons are seen lower right.*　　　　　　　　　　　　　　　　　　　　　　　　　　　*[Newport City Libraries]*

*The dam and valve tower of Wentwood reservoir, 23 July 1990.*　　　　　　　　*[Allan C Baker]*

career at Nine Elms and Eastleigh with the London and South Western Railway. However, in 1893-94 Drummond was designing and building small locomotives at Govan, Glasgow, notably 2ft gauge locomotives for special duties in Glasgow's Dawsholm gasworks.

One of the two locomotives the Corporation inherited from the Young period here did not give satisfaction and in or about November 1896 it was hauled away to Newport by Robert Wynn - still a familiar name today in heavy road haulage - and a six wheel standard gauge engine (Fox Walker 264) was secured in exchange, to be followed in October 1898 by a newly built six-coupled locomotive (Avonside 1395), also for standard gauge. In March 1899, the other 3ft gauge loco derived from Young was sold to C D Phillips, the Newport machinery dealer, and after this the standard gauge prevailed for the site railways. (Readers should be aware that this is HDB's interpretation of the locomotive history in the early period. Martin Potts came to different conclusions on studying the Corporation minutes. This issue is amplified later.)

Even today, the roads to the site are little more than winding country lanes. The six-wheeled locomotive obtained in 1896 was to be hauled up by horses but instead, and unlicensed, it came under its own power on the road. This was irregular and it must have been an embarrassment to the Corporation Waterworks Department when their licensing colleagues, or those of the County Council, demanded payment of £10 for a retrospective traction engine license on behalf of the erring railway locomotive. After representations, the fee was waived.

The nearest railway station was at Magor, on the GWR South Wales main line, and on 21 September 1896, the railway company agreed to provide special facilities there for the unloading of plant and materials. Later, in January 1899, an 8hp steam traction engine and four wagons, doubtless trailers, were ordered from John Fowler of Leeds, their engine 7969 of type B4, a compound, delivered in March 1899. This engine ran mainly between Newport and Wentwood.

The traction engine and wagons were sold to C D Phillips for £506 in January 1903, and the engine was with E W Wright of Alton, Hants, in 1904. It has not been established whether the heaviest and most constant traffic by road, namely cement for concrete making, was brought from Newport or Magor, but it is reasonable to presume that the Fowler engine and wagons conveyed it; the period 1899-1902 would correspond with the main demand for cement at Wentwood.

As least two Whittaker steam navvies were acquired for digging material for the embankment. Horses were hired for use on and about the embankment, hauling the ubiquitous "dobbin carts". These three-wheeled vehicles were pulled by two horses, one each side of the centre shaft. At least eighteen were bought in 1900-02, the Gloucester Wagon Company and the Wigan Wagon Company being the suppliers.

Suitable clay could not be found at site but was dug on the lands of Mr W. S. Lang in the Cwm valley, to the eastward beyond Gray hill. In order to convey the clay, an overhead cableway of about two miles was built by Ropeways Syndicate Limited and put into service in mid 1900. It terminated at an unloading station described as "some distance beyond the top end of the reservoir on the line of the tunnel near shaft No.2". The ropeway was driven by the Corporation's portable steam engine, possibly the Ruston, Proctor machine offered new to them in 1897. The tunnel referred to was two and a half miles long, driven through below the northern slopes of Gray hill to divert the waters of the Castroggy and other brooks under the hill and into Wentwood reservoir. The main standard gauge construction railway is believed to have run from the quarry, where standard gauge sleepers have been found, and the depot previously mentioned across the public road and by way of the present site access road to the embankment. A fresh route, probably a diversion, was created for it in December 1902, following the public road on the west side, in order to ease the gradient as the bank rose in height. To the east of the

*The castellated intake to the 2½ mile tunnel which channels the Castroggy Brook water to the Wentwood reservoir, 3 June 1990.* [Harold D Bowtell]

*The eastern bank of Wentwood reservoir with Gray Hill behind. The lighter coloured earth in front of the wood indicates the course of the construction railway. 23 July 1990.* [Allen C Baker]

reservoir site the railway ran along the hillside and construction views show it well above the water level when the lake was filling and perhaps half full. Yankee-type tip wagons and a steam crane are depicted on this line, which is the probable route to the clay unloading station. It should however be noted that there is also a surviving alignment capable of carrying a standard gauge line, above high water but below the public road, on the west side.

The impounding of water commenced in December 1903 and inauguration by the Mayor of Newport, Councillor Colonel W Clifford Phillips, was on 31 May 1904, the lake having a water capacity of 410 million gallons and top water level about 450ft o.d. The total cost of the project was £402,000 - including the cost of the eight-mile delivery aqueduct to Beechwood Road, Newport - a staggering sum compared to James Young's original tender of less than £100,000. The Works Manager, Mr Macdonald, was unfortunate when his house and effects and site office (but not the drawings) were destroyed by fire on 19 April 1904. He resigned on 3 October 1904, on completion of work at the site. C. D. Phillips, Junior, (the auctioneer son of the Newport–based machinery dealer) conducted a final sale of plant on 29-30 October (*Contract Journal*, 7/9/1904).

As mentioned previously, there is some difficulty in interpreting the Corporation's minutes concerning the plant taken over from James Young. Two locomotives were involved but there has been disagreement over whether these were both of 3ft gauge (as HDB believes; and therefore one remains unidentified) or whether one was of 3ft gauge and one standard gauge (as suggested by Martin Potts) - the latter being Manning Wardle 904 listed here. The locomotive notes presented here should thus be read with this uncertainty in mind. Readers wishing to follow the debate between Mr Potts and HDB on the interpretation of the minutes in this respect are advised to read *The Industrial Locomotive* N°. 72 (1994) pp. 74-79.

### 3ft gauge locomotive(s)

No. 1    0-4-0 saddle tank    oc 7in x 10in
    by D. Drummond & Son, built 1896 - new here; ordered by James Young but delivered to Newport Corporation, c.4/1896, after Young's withdrawal from the project. The locomotive is thought to have been designed for work in tunnels or other restricted clearances (being provided with a removable chimney). It was sold to C. D. Phillips, the Newport dealer, for £325 in 3/1899 and was later (1907-1914) with Morrison & Mason on their Chew Valley Reservoir contract, W. Yorks, for Stalybridge Corporation.

Possibly another unidentified locomotive of this gauge here (see text)

### Standard gauge locomotives

-    0-4-0 saddle tank    oc 12in x 18in
    by Manning Wardle 904 of 1884 - new 2/1884 to J. E. Billups, the Cardiff-based contractor, as FRANK and used on his Cardiff New Dry Dock contract of 1883-1884. Billups' plant was for sale in 3/1892 on his retirement and by c.1894 the loco was in the ownership of James Young, possibly coming to Wentwood with him. This may have been the locomotive deemed unsatisfactory at Wentwood by the Corporation and may have passed to dealer T Davies in 11/1896 in part exchange for the six-coupled Fox Walker 264. Later with contractor F C Caffin probably on his Pilning Jct - Avonmouth (GWR) job, 1896-1900. It was sold to the Avonside Engine Co, 6/1899, who repaired and sold it to the Denby Coal & Iron Co Ltd for their Denby Iron Works, near Derby, on 19/9/1899. Spares were ordered from Avonside for the loco on 7/3/1900. Her subsequent history is unknown.

- 0-6-0 saddle tank    oc 13in x 20in

    by Fox Walker  264 of 1875 - probably new to W F Lawrence, a contractor building the Cheltenham - Bourton-on the-Water section of the GWR Cheltenham & Banbury Direct Rly, 1874 – 1878, as BARON. Later with John Waddell, contractor, on the Llanelly & Mynydd Mawr Rly construction, 1880-1883; still later said to have been with Appleby & Lawton, possibly finishing off the Whitland & Cardigan Rly, c.1883-1886; acquired by Newport Corporation from dealer T Davies in 10/1896 for £425 plus a traded-in loco (MW 904). For sale at the closing auction by C D Phillips Jnr., 30/9/1904, (*Contract Journal*, 7/9/1904); still unsold in 9/1905; possibly to C D Phillips, the Newport dealer, after this date becoming his EMLYN N°.101; no subsequent trace, but possibly with (iron and steel maker) "Nettlefolds" at an unknown location. Guest, Keen & Nettlefolds Ltd had a plant on the east bank of the Usk at Newport, and another at Rogerstone.

CHARLES LYNE  0-6-0 saddle tank    oc 14in x 20in

    by Avonside  1395 of  1898 – ordered by the Corporation 8/1898 and left the builder's works for Magor station 8/11/1898 at a cost of £1,040. For sale in the 30/9/1904 auction; to Sheepbridge Coal & Iron Co. Ltd., as '5', by 21/12/1905 (from spares order). Spares were ordered again in 2 and 11/1911 for 'Sheepbridge Ironstone Mines, Frodingham & Scunthorpe, GCR, Lincs. The locomotive subsequently had a long career with this company at the Sheepbridge Ironworks and Glapwell Colliery, both in Derbys; Desborough Ironstone Mines, Northants; and Langwith Colliery, Derbys; it was at Glapwell Colliery again on Vesting Day, 1/1/1947, and so became the property of the National Coal Board, East Midlands Division, No.1 Area; it was transferred to Grasmoor Colliery, Derbys, and scrapped there in late 1953.

A 10inch, four-coupled, locomotive was to be sold at Wentwood on 30/6/1904 (per *Western Mail* 28/5/1904 and *Contract Journal* 8/6/1904). This description does not fit any of the locomotives described here. No further details are known.

*Avonside 1395 of 1898 came new to Newport Corporation at Wentwood named* CHARLES LYNE *after the Chairman of the Water Committee. Seen here some years later as '5' of the Sheepbridge Coal & Iron Co Ltd, Derbyshire.*                                                                                     *[Frank Jones]*

# Talybont

The main line of the former Brecon and Merthyr Railway has been encountered around Pontsticill Junction and again at its Torpantau summit when studying relics of the associated waterworks railways of Merthyr Corporation and the Taf Fechan Water Supply Board (see Chapter 3). North of Torpantau station (1,310ft) it passed through a short tunnel, falling at 1 in 78, and then descended for approximately seven miles on a continuous gradient of 1 in 37 and 1 in 38 - one of the fiercest banks on a British railway - to reach Talybont-on-Usk station (385ft). The line was opened in 1863, single track, and closed in 1964.

The story of Talybont Reservoir has been admirably told by the Rev David Tipper in his book *The Talybont Saga* (published by Welsh Water in 1993). Saga is the appropriate word. Some twenty-three years passed between the determination of the need for enhanced water supplies and the opening of the reservoir just before the outbreak of World War II.

In 1916 Mr H Tremelling, the Newport Borough Engineer, and John Francis Jupp, a Newport-based civil engineer, were instructed to report on the town's water needs and, with a view to meeting those needs, a number of possible reservoir sites. They reported in January 1917 that Newport's consumption had doubled in the previous twenty years. This increase in demand was in no small measure due to the establishment and growth of iron and steel mills in the town. These comprised Nettlefolds' Castle Works at Rogerstone (opened by 1887), John Lysaght Limited's Orb Works (1898), Nettlefolds' Imperial Wire Mills (c.1902) and the British Mannesmann Tube Company Limited's works (c.1916).

The two engineers considered four reservoir sites, three in the Black Mountains at Cwmdu, Grwynefechan and at Capel-y-Ffin (near Llanthony Abbey) and one in the Caerfanell Valley near Talybont. This last was the recommended option. A second report commissioned during May 1917 from G H Hill & Sons, of Manchester and Westminster, water engineers, endorsed the findings of the first report.

Alderman Thomas Parry, the Chairman of the town's Water Committee, faced enormous difficulties persuading his fellow citizens of the wisdom of such a scheme. The plan was approved by the Borough Council but rejected first by ratepayers at a Statutory Meeting and then by voters in a Town Poll in January 1919. In an attempt to break the deadlock a third report was commissioned in 1919 from Mr W A Tait, of Edinburgh, the enthusiastic consulting engineer who had been responsible for Edinburgh's Talla scheme some twenty years earlier. Tait was asked to adjudicate between three options: buying in water from Merthyr Tydfil Corporation, who were eager to sell their surplus to neighbouring authorities; buying in from the Great Western Railway's 'Big Spring' at the Severn Tunnel, pumped via Wentwood Reservoir; or proceeding with the council's own Talybont scheme. Tait recommended the latter, but argued that, instead of providing a huge dammed reservoir in the valley down the side of which the B&MR ran, an intake weir on the Caerfanell river near Fynnon-wen farm, up the valley above Talybont, would capture enough water to meet Newport's needs for a number of years. Tait estimated that this modified scheme would cost approximately £600,000 against the £1,541,000 estimated for the reservoir option.

The scheme in this form was approved by a Town Poll and proceeded on this basis although the subsequent Newport Corporation Act of 4 August 1920 still allowed for the provision of a Caerfanell Reservoir at a later date. An important feature of both the original and the modified schemes was an aqueduct more than thirty miles long to take the water from the collecting point to Malpas Road, Newport, and including a service reservoir at Croes-y-Mwyalch, near Llantarnam, (grid reference ST

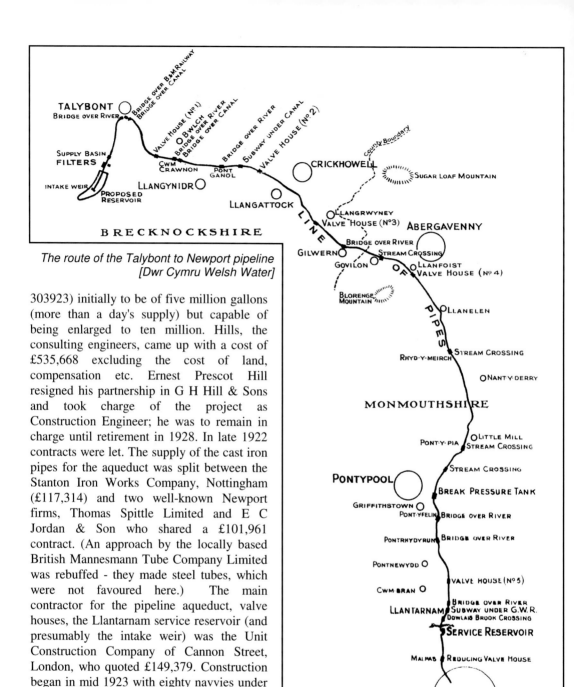

*The route of the Talybont to Newport pipeline*
*[Dwr Cymru Welsh Water]*

303923) initially to be of five million gallons (more than a day's supply) but capable of being enlarged to ten million. Hills, the consulting engineers, came up with a cost of £535,668 excluding the cost of land, compensation etc. Ernest Prescot Hill resigned his partnership in G H Hill & Sons and took charge of the project as Construction Engineer; he was to remain in charge until retirement in 1928. In late 1922 contracts were let. The supply of the cast iron pipes for the aqueduct was split between the Stanton Iron Works Company, Nottingham (£117,314) and two well-known Newport firms, Thomas Spittle Limited and E C Jordan & Son who shared a £101,961 contract. (An approach by the locally based British Mannesmann Tube Company Limited was rebuffed - they made steel tubes, which were not favoured here.) The main contractor for the pipeline aqueduct, valve houses, the Llantarnam service reservoir (and presumably the intake weir) was the Unit Construction Company of Cannon Street, London, who quoted £149,379. Construction began in mid 1923 with eighty navvies under a ruthless chief ganger, Charlie Sheasby. Thirty of these men had walked to the site from Birmingham.

A vital piece of equipment was the Parsons Steam Trench Cutter invented by an American, Allen Parsons. This machine could average 150 yards of trench, up to fifteen feet deep, per day. Its value is self-evident when we consider that the pipeline aqueduct was to be 33 miles long. Construction work was completed in March 1926 and Alderman Tom Parry inaugurated the works in a ceremony held on 29 September 1927. Locomotive powered railways are not known to have been used at the intake weir

*The delightful setting of Newport's Talybont reservoir, seen here from the east, 25 May 2004.*
*[Geoffrey Hill]*

site, though a photograph exists of a rail-mounted steam crane of apparent standard gauge in use at Fynnon-wen. However, a note in the Water Committee minutes of 6/10/1924 reveals that a small loco was at that time employed hauling away spoil at the Llantarnam service reservoir. There is also a note in HDB's papers that Geo. Pauling & Company Limited used a two foot gauge locomotive (believed to be steam) on a "Newport-Talybont pipeline contract, c.1922". These intriguing references may well refer to the same event and locomotive but fail to explain why Paulings, a large and prestigious firm, would appear to be acting as sub-contractors here. Perhaps they merely hired a locomotive to the Unit Construction Company for the duration of the job.

By May 1928, all was not well. Major W E Lloyd MC, who had come to the project as the Unit Construction Company's engineer and agent in 1920 and had been appointed Newport's Borough and Water Engineer in 1924, reported that in times of flood 100 million gallons per day could run to waste at the weir but that in drought little or no water was extracted. Serious consideration was given once more, in 1929-1931, to the use of Severn Tunnel water. However, the idea of constructing a reservoir was resurrected and gained ascendancy. Six variants were studied and the option chosen was a lake of some 2,500 gallons with a dam length of 1,345ft. This was not the original Caerfanell Reservoir proposal and location. The engineers had decided that the site of the proposed dam there was unsound; instead, the dam was to be a little nearer Talybont station (at grid reference SO 1052040 about two miles to the south west of the latter), although about two thirds of the area of the reservoir would be in common with the Caerfanell proposal. The project would also necessitate the realignment of two miles of road to the west side of the new reservoir.

A grant was to be given to the Corporation under a public works Act of 1930, which sought to relieve unemployment. Under this scheme the government was to pay the men's wages, seemingly a windfall for the Corporation, but one that was to prove controversial in the town and in the council chamber. Because of the location of the proposed reservoir, the rural wage rate, 10½ pence per hour (pre-decimalisation), was laid down by the government, although the plan was that the labourers would

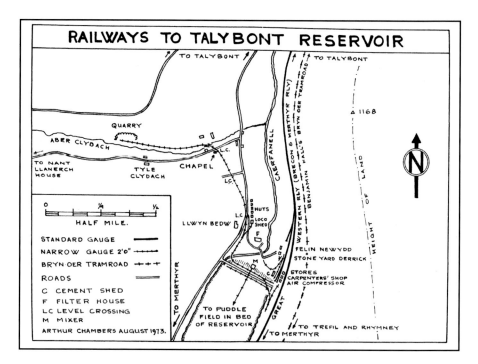

RAILWAYS TO TALYBONT RESERVOIR

TO TALYBONT
TO TALYBONT

QUARRY

ABER CLYDACH

TO NANT
LLANERCH
HOUSE

TYLE
CLYDACH

CHAPEL

HALF MILE.

STANDARD GAUGE

NARROW GAUGE 2'0"

BRYN OER TRAMROAD

ROADS

C CEMENT SHED
F FILTER HOUSE
LC LEVEL CROSSING
M MIXER

ARTHUR CHAMBERS AUGUST 1973.

LLWYN BEDW

HUTS
LOCO
SHED

FELIN NEWYDD
STONE YARD DERRICK

STORES
CARPENTERS' SHOP
AIR COMPRESSOR

TO PUDDLE
FIELD IN BED
OF RESERVOIR

TO MERTHYR

TO TREFIL AND RHYMNEY

CAERFANELL

WESTERN RLY (BRECON & MERTHYR RLY)
BENJAMIN HALL'S BRYN OER TRAMROAD

HEIGHT OF LAND

GREAT

be overwhelmingly from Newport. The unemployed and their supporters felt they should get the urban rate of 14½ pence, especially bearing in mind their likely travel and lodging costs.

Under the government scheme monies were administered by the Unemployed Government Grants (UGG) committee and a Government Supervisory Engineer, Mr F W Macauley, was imposed to 'sign off' on important aspects so as to ensure that public money was well spent. Six weeks of negotiation followed the uproar on the wage issue, the outcome of which was that the UGG committee agreed to pay a rate of 12½ pence per hour plus free travel and lodging. This proved acceptable and the Corporation agreed to proceed in May 1931.

The Corporation estimate included £2,692 for a railway, leaving the GWR (B&MR) 2,840 yards north-west from the north-east corner of Pentir Rhiw station. This was the station about half way up the famous Torpantau bank. The Corporation's railway, installed in May 1932, trailed off the former B&MR to the left of a descending northbound train and extended 2 furlongs 9 chains (just over a third of a mile), with sidings just above the east end of the proposed dam.

Twenty-one firms tendered for the reservoir contract in April 1932. By June the Waterworks Committee had reduced this number to two. These were G P Trentham, of Birmingham, whose price was £320,000, and John McColville, usually referred to at the time as an "Abergavenny public works contractor". McColville lived at The Cloisters, Abergavenny, but his registered office was at Gordon Chambers, 31 Queen Street, Cardiff. He tendered £367,000. Trenthams have been well-known contractors down to the present time. On this occasion they refused to sign the contract forms as presented and requested modifications to the project to achieve their tendered price. This did not sit well with the Newport Committee, who knew what they wanted doing. They gave the contract to McColville on 14 July 1932. His later correspondence was on notepaper headed "Reservoir Contract, Talybont-on-Usk".

John McColville had held a responsible position on the Catcleugh Reservoir scheme (Newcastle and Gateshead Water Company, direct labour) and then from 1904 he was with Tynemouth

Corporation as their Resident Engineer at Fontburn Reservoir construction, also in Northumberland. He next supervised, for the Derwent Valley Water Board, the building of Ambergate Reservoir and water mains and tunnels in Derbyshire (work done by contractors in 1907-1910). He was with Koppers Coke Oven Company constructing coke ovens, including the ones at Ebbw Vale Steelworks; and from c.1926 to c.1929, as a contractor in his own right, built the Glyn Neath to Banwen road, in the present day West Glamorgan, as part of the Depression-era Glamorgan Inter-Valley Roads Scheme. He put down roots in South Wales, setting up the Cardiff office mentioned earlier, and his daughter married the future Lord Brecon. However, he was still active in the north, being engaged from December 1928 to June 1932 on Contract N°.2 of the new twelve-mile road through the Pass of Glencoe for Argyll County Council. (It is interesting that, in September 1932, W Probert Jnr., presumably a Welshman, a locomotive driver employed by McColville at Bridge of Orchy, his railhead for Glencoe, was considered for a job, in a supervisory capacity, at Talybont).

A local firm, L J Speight & Company, won the contract for the two-mile realignment of the Torpantau road. This was carried out between July 1931 and midsummer 1932. The road was opened at Talybont by Alderman Parry on 28 July 1932 and on the same occasion the first sod of the reservoir was turned by the Mayor, Griffith Jones. McColville set to work and saw his job through to completion. (He was to be still finishing off in the Spring of 1939.) By the end of 1932, 171 men were at work, all but sixteen of them bussed up weekly from Newport, as had been the men working on the road diversion, the GWR being unable to provide an acceptable and cost effective passenger service from Newport to Pentir Rhiw. By September 1933, three hundred men were employed, the highest number reached.

*River diversion culvert and tail bay under construction at Talybont 1933. 'Simplex' locomotive and tracked steam shovel at centre.* [Dwr Cymru Welsh Water]

*Impounding at Talybont is well under way and the valve tower almost complete in this November 1938 view. The access road is in place but 2ft gauge track is still in use along the whole length of the dam.* [Dwr Cymru Welsh Water]

Traffic coming on the GWR for the site was detached at Talybont station, propelled up the bank by the railway company's engine and placed in the Corporation's siding near their cement store. The contractor did not use a locomotive on this limited standard gauge layout but moved individual wagons by means of a steam crane with crawler tracks. Considerable amounts of high-quality facing and masonry stone came in by rail from Craig-yr-Hesg quarries, near Pontypridd. Puddle clay, in large quantities, was to have come in this way from Dowlais Top but this was obviated by the finding of good clay in the reservoir bed near Ty-newydd farm, one and a quarter miles above the dam site. Cement came by rail. Other stone was won from two quarries opened out nearby; one in the Clydach Valley (Aberclydach Quarry), the other on the east side of the railway (Railway Quarry) near the site of the dam.

There was an extensive narrow gauge railway layout on this job, but in place of the fairly substantial 3ft gauge tracks and sturdy steam locomotives, found on so many similar projects down to and including the nineteen thirties, McColville used light 2ft gauge track and internal combustion locomotives. The contractor's yard, with cement shed, carpenters' and fitters' shops, compressor house, stone and timber yards and stocks of coal and sand adjoined the standard gauge sidings, above the site on the east of the valley. A narrow gauge incline (three rails at the top) descended from this yard to the working area of the trench excavation and embankment construction. Later, the tracks were able to cross the bank as it was built up. A long branch ran up the valley bottom to the clay field. At the west end of the site the main narrow gauge tracks curved northwards to the locomotive shed and the "navvy village". There were twelve huts for men, a policeman's hut and a club. Beyond the village the line struck across the road and fields and over two lanes, the second being that from Aber village to Nantllanerch House, crossed beside the chapel; then over the stream and up through the wooded estate of Mrs Gladys Garnons-Williams of Glanclydach, to reach Aberclydach Quarry which was worked mainly to provide pitching stone for the water face of the dam. (Mrs Garnons-Williams

*The valve tower at Talybont, in finest 'municipal baronial' style, 25 May 2004.*            *[Geoffrey Hill]*

was still resident at Glanclydach, almost opposite the chapel, until 1978.) This attractive quarry branch was a mile or so in length from the site village and was brought into use by October 1932, when some fifty trucks of stone came down daily. Subsequent working was apparently intermittent. (Beyond the quarry, at a higher level, is a supplementary intake - with a pipeline to augment the reservoir - constructed by contract in 1955-1956 under the authority of an Act of 1953.)

The 2ft gauge tracks totalled seven miles in all. There were 133 wagons and 13 petrol locomotives, according to reports dated 1932-1933. Two locomotives are recalled as being by Dorman (engine makers) and there were many by "Simplex" (Motor Rail and Tramcar Company Limited, of Bedford). Steam figured in the shape of at least seven rail-mounted steam cranes on apparently standard gauge track that worked on the dam and overflow etc. and three steam excavators with half-cubic-yard buckets. (There was an internal combustion powered dragline excavator, also of half-cubic-yard capacity.) A steam road roller with "sheep's foot" rolls was used for compacting the dam and other earthworks (illustrated on page 102).

The work drew to a close in 1938, with impounding of water commencing in the spring of that year and the reservoir overflowing for the first time on 6 April 1939. The dam is 1,400ft long with a maximum height of 97ft above ground and the trench goes down to 85ft maximum below ground. Top water level is at 620ft above o.d. and capacity 2,567 million gallons - a huge artificial lake just over two miles long. Twenty-one farms comprising a total of 3,220 acres of land had been purchased by the Corporation for the project - some for the lake and buildings themselves, of course, but much to prevent contamination by farming activities of the watercourses leading into the reservoir. Formal opening by the Mayor, Alderman John Wardell, was on 29 June 1939. By happy coincidence the Mayor was also Chairman of the Waterworks Committee, having succeeded Alderman Tom Parry, who died in office aged eighty three, in May 1935. (Alderman Parry had been Chairman of the Committee from 1910 and had started his career on the Monmouthshire Railway & Canal Company in 1867!) Major Wilfred W Marsden MC, who had been Resident Engineer for the Corporation on part of the earlier intake weir project in the 1920s, was their Construction Engineer and Manager for the duration of the reservoir project.

A second pipeline connecting the reservoir with Newport was laid between 1938 and 1947. Its route largely followed that of the 1927 pipeline except between Llantarnam and Newport where an alternative alignment fed an additional service reservoir at Ladyhill.

Talybont was probably the biggest dam construction undertaken without steam locomotives since the era of steam light railways dawned in earnest in the 1870s. It exemplified the brief interregnum of extensive light 2ft gauge lines and internal combustion locomotives on such work. Use of the standard gauge branch, referred to as 'Newport Corporation Siding' by the Railway Clearing House, was discontinued in May 1940.

*A 2½ ton 20 hp Motor Rail ('Simplex') petrol locomotive at work in the construction of the overflow channel for the Talybont dam in 1937.*        *[Dwr Cymru Welsh Water]*

## 2ft gauge locomotives

See the text earlier regarding a note on the use of a locomotive on the pipeline contract and Llantarnam service reservoir, c.1922-1926. The following were definitely used at Talybont by John McColville, 1932-1939:

F C Hibberd      4wPM      No.1927 of 1935      20hp
     New 5/1935; a reconditioned Motor Rail 'Simplex' loco; said to be 'ex J J Johnston, contractor'.
     No subsequent history known.

Motor Rail      4wPM      3978      1936      20hp
     Ordered by McColville 2/10/1936; ex makers, 6/10/1936.
     No subsequent history known.

Motor Rail      4wPM      4804      1934      20hp
     New to PLH (Petrol Loco Hirers Ltd) ordered 23/1/1935; ordered by McColville 2/10/1936;
     ex makers 6/10/1936. No subsequent history known.

The following are not confirmed at Talybont but were in McColville's ownership at the dates shown and were very possibly used there:

| Motor Rail | 4wPM | 2076 | 1922 | 20hp |

New (as 60cm gauge) to PLH (Petrol Loco Hirers Ltd) from stock 28/4/1922; dispatched to Mactaggart & Co., contractors, Mosspark Sidings, Corkerhill, Glasgow, on the same day; sold by PLH to McColville for £200, 2/12/1926, for his Glyn Neath-Banwen road contract, West Glam, c.1926-c1930; (part of the Glamorgan Inter-Valley Roads Scheme). No subsequent history known.

| Motor Rail | 4wPM | 2148 | 1921 | 20hp |

New (as 60cm gauge) to PLH from stock 28/9/1921; dispatched to Borough Surveyor, County Borough of Tynemouth, North Shields Station, Northumbs; sold (by PLH) to McColville for £200, 2/12/1926 for Glyn Neath-Banwen. No subsequent history known.

| Motor Rail | 4wPM | 2287 | 1924 | 20hp |

New (as 60 cm gauge) to PLH from stock 6/5/1924; dispatched same day to ?; sold (by PLH) to McColville, 2/12/1926, for Glyn Neath-Banwen. No subsequent history known.

| Motor Rail | 4wPM | 3849 | 1927 | 20hp |

New to PLH 25/5/1927; used (by Manchester Corporation?) at Heaton Park Reservoir construction, Manchester; sold by PLH to McColville, 7/11/1929, for Glyn Neath-Banwen; by 2/1950 as 2ft 6in gauge with Fred Watkins (Engineers) Ltd, Sling Plant Depot, Milkwall, Gloucs, via War Department usage.

| Motor Rail | 4wPM | 3882 | | 20hp |

New to Cleveland Bridge & Engineering Co. Ltd. (of Darlington) and dispatched to Widney Manor, Birmingham, for their GWR Olton-Lapworth widening contract c.1931-1933; with McColville by 26/4/1933. No subsequent history known.

| Motor Rail | 4wPM | 4550 | 1929 | 20hp |

New (as 60cm gauge) to PLH, 27/3/1929; sold to McColville for Glyn Neath-Banwen, 2/11/1930; with Fred Watkins (Engineers) Ltd, Sling Plant Depot, Milkwall, Gloucs, by 12/9/1940.

*A steam 'navvy' and 40 hp Motor Rail ('Simplex') petrol locomotive seen working on the overflow channel at Talybont dam.*          *[Dwr Cymru Welsh Water]*

*The compound steam roller built by Thomas Green & Sons and fitted with "sheep's foot" rolls used to aid compaction of the Talybont dam embankment.*     *[Dwr Cymru Welsh Water]*

Motor Rail      4wPM      5232      1930      20/35hp
New to PLH (Petrol Loco Hirers Ltd) 15/11/1930; converted from 2½ ton to 4ton loco and sold by makers to Durham County Water Board, Burnhope Reservoir construction, Wearhead, Co. Durham, 26/1/1932; to McColville at date unknown. No subsequent history known.

Motor Rail      4wPM      5310      1931      20/35hp
New to Sir Robert McAlpine & Sons, Acton Lane contract, near Chiswick Park Station, London W5, 23/4/1931; with McColville by 8/11/1935 (spares order). No subsequent history known.

Ruston & Hornsby      4wDM      168791      1933?      16hp
New (?) to McColville by 23/6/1933; returned to makers by 2/7/1933 (on trial and rejected?);
later with East Surrey Water Co. at ?, 11/9/1933.

All nine of the locomotives listed as "possibles" here *COULD* have been at Talybont in the years 1932-1933. That leaves at least four of the thirteen mentioned in the 1932-1933 reports unaccounted for. Some of these, from textual and photographic evidence in *The Talybont Saga*, were 40hp formerly armoured or protected locos, none of which appear in our list. The three locomotives definitely known to have been at Talybont (FH 1927, MRs 3978, and 4804) arrived after 1932-1933 and are thus additional to the thirteen in the reports of those dates. Any further information from readers on McColville's locomotives at Talybont (or elsewhere) would be very welcome.

All of the reservoirs considered in this chapter will have passed to the control of the Gwent Water Board as from 1 April 1970.

# Chapter 8

## Other projects using railways

*Nantmelin, Nanthir & Nantmoel Reservoirs*
*for Aberdare Urban District Council and its predecessors*

The Aberdare Waterworks Company was formed in 1856 and obtained an Act of Parliament in 1858 permitting the construction of Nantmelin (or Bwllfa Graig) Reservoir (at grid reference SN 973027) in the village of Cwmdare. Work commenced in October of that year and was completed in September 1859. The top water level is at 710ft above o.d.. The work included filter beds at Monk Street, Aberdare, connected to the nine-million-gallon reservoir by pipes running along the formation of the Vale of Neath Railway's Dare and Aman branch (later GWR). The contractor for this project has not yet been identified. In 1872 the Aberdare Local Board of Health purchased the Waterworks Company having obtained an Act allowing them to do so in 1870. Ownership passed to the newly formed Aberdare UDC in 1894. The Taf Fechan Water Supply Act of 1921, as mentioned earlier, included Aberdare Corporation within its constitution as a member but left it with control of the waterworks in its own area.

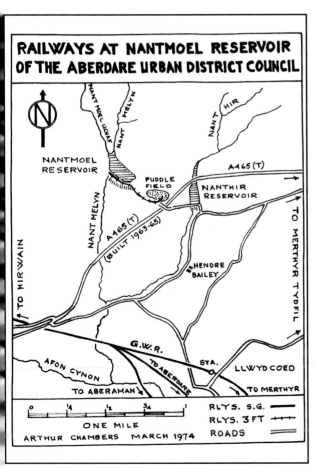

The rapid population growth in the district as the coal trade developed caused the Local Board to promote Nanthir Reservoir (dam at grid reference SN 989067); this reservoir is now called Hendre Beili after the farm that lies to its south. It was built from 1872 - c.1875 under the powers granted by the Local Board's Waterworks Act of 1870. The engineer for the project was the well-known J F Bateman of Manchester but again the contractor responsible is not known. It is a curiously narrow lake of 40 million gallons, with an earth dam and puddle core, occupying the valley of the Nant Hir stream about three miles north west of Aberdare. The top water level is at 850ft above o.d.. The Heads of the Valleys road, built in the early nineteen-sixties, crosses this slim reservoir.

Immediately to the west of it is Nantmoel Reservoir (dam at grid reference SN 981070) of 67 million gallons capacity initially, fed by the Nant Melyn and Nant Moel Uchaf streams, with an earth embankment (with puddle core) on its longest (southern) side. The top water level is at 864ft above o.d.. (Two and a half miles further west is the Penderyn

*Aberdare UDC's Nantmoel reservoir pictured on 25 May 2004*          *[Geoffrey Hill]*

reservoir of Mountain Ash UDC, the building of which has been discussed in Chapter 5.) Nantmoel was built c.1897-1899, under the authority of the Aberdare Local Water Board Act of 1894.

No evidence is as yet forthcoming concerning the use of railways at Nantmelin or Nanthir but 3ft gauge tracks were certainly used at Nantmoel. It has been suggested in the past that the Urban District Council carried out this project using direct labour, but it has been established that contractor William Jones of Neath was engaged here. However, the UDC appears to have owned the two locomotives listed and some of the other plant, although Jones may have used locomotives of his own at the site (see the note on the completion sales later). The puddle field, which provided clay, is between Nantmoel, and Nanthir and a 3ft gauge line was used to convey the clay to the bank, about half a mile. The tracks may possibly have encircled the reservoir site. One locomotive is positively identified at Nantmoel: -

NANTMELYN    0-4-0 saddle tank   oc 8in x 12in
> by Hudswell Clarke 424 built for stock in 1894; dispatched new on 11/2/1897 with the date 1897 on her plates to Aberdare UDC with this painted name (named after the stream). After sale from Nantmoel, she passed to William Kennedy, contractor of Partick, Glasgow, and then worked on John Best's reservoir project for Falkirk & Larbert Water Trustees at Drumbowie, near Denny, Stirlingshire, in the years 1901-c.1907; she was probably the loco at Best's Craigleith Quarry, Edinburgh, in 12/1906 and definitely was with Best as his 'N°.20' on the Delph Reservoir job for Bolton Corporation from c.1908 to c.1916. To Henry Boot & Sons (London) Ltd on their Trumpington (MoM) contract, Cambs, c.1918; to Muirhead, MacDonald, Wilson & Co Ltd, Fulham plant depot, London; from c.1919 to 1922 with the Executor of L. P. Nott/Nott, Brodie at Blaen-y-

Cwm as RUBY (see later this Chapter); at the Taf Fechan Water Board's site at Pontsticill still as RUBY from c.6/1922 (see Chapter 3); then to A. R. Adams, the Newport dealer, after 9/1927 and by 4/1929; to Richard Baillie, of Haddington, East Lothian, after 6/1931 and by 2/1932 and used by him on his Hopes Reservoir contract, Gifford, E. Lothian, 1929-1935, and on the Derwent Valley Water Board's Ladybower Reservoir, Derbys, (see *Manchester & the Peak*), 1935-1945. Believed scrapped here after some years of disuse, c.1949/50 - a good career in waterworks engineering.

On 3 and 4 October 1899 when plant from this contract was auctioned on behalf of Aberdare UDC (*The Engineer* 15/9/1899, *Contract Journal* 20/9/1899), NANTMELYN was in company with a second 0-4-0 locomotive described as by "Baker of Cardiff". No further details are known, but "Baker" is presumably P Baker of Albion Works, East Moors Road, the well-known locomotive dealer and repairer. Whether he built it or merely rebuilt/overhauled it makes for interesting speculation.

It is interesting to note that at a slightly earlier date, 21-22/9/1899 an auction of plant lying 'at Llwydcoed, Aberdare and at Neath on completion of Aberdare new waterworks' was to be held on the instructions of the contractor William Jones (*Western Mail*, 19/8/1899 and 16/9/1899). This was said to include locomotives too, but perhaps this was a "misunderstanding" over ownership of the UDC's engines. It is clear that the possibility that Jones operated his own locomotives here should not be lost sight of. Another contractor/sub-contractor named R C Brebner has also been associated with the Nantmoel site (see *Western Mail*, 29/5/1897).

NANTMELYN *(Hudswell Clarke 424 of 1897) came new to Aberdare UDC and enjoyed a very long life at a number of locations including Pontsticill (chapter 3) and Blaen-y-Cwm (see later this chapter) as RUBY. Nant Melyn is the name of the stream that feeds Nantmoel reservoir.* [Frank Jones Collection]

Water supplies to Aberdare were augmented in 1913 when, by arrangement with Merthyr Tydfil Corporation, a pipeline was built from Merthyr's Upper Neuadd Reservoir (see Chapter 3) to the locality. And further, (according to Mr Tom Williams, the resident keeper at the site in the 1970s), the Nantmoel dam was raised in the 1930s. Narrow gauge diesel locomotives were used on this project but details of these are not available. Dai Oliver, later to be chauffeur of the Aberdare UDC official limousine, drove diesel locomotives here.

## Water for Pontypridd and Rhondda from the Hills above the Rhondda Valleys

### *Castell Nos and Lluest (or Llewst) Wen Reservoirs*
### *at the head of the Rhondda Fach*

The Pontypridd Water Works Company, formed by local people in 1861, originally took its water from Darren Ddu and springs in Lan Wood north of the town centre. The company gave place in 1910 to the Pontypridd and Rhondda Joint Water Board - controlled by Pontypridd UDC (who elected five members) and Rhondda UDC (seven members) - and that in turn, in 1922, to the Taf Fechan Water Supply Board.

The topmost village in the Rhondda Fach (Little Rhondda) Valley is Maerdy (formerly Mardy), which was reached by a branch passenger train service of the Taff Vale Railway from Porth on the main Rhondda line from Treherbert. A colliery railway extended beyond Maerdy passenger station (which closed from 15/6/1964) and the former goods station to Mardy colliery. The colliery retained its own locomotives until 1987, and was the last in the Rhondda to close, in December 1990. The first two Mardy pits dated back to 1875, N°.3 pit was sunk in 1893 and the No.4 in 1914, these last two higher up the valley. In October 1940 the colliery was closed, with only maintenance done, until production resumed in March 1949 at N°s. 3 & 4 pits. Around 1954 the colliery secured a new lease of life through modernisation and development by the NCB. The previous owner had been Powell Duffryn Limited, who took over here in 1939 from Bwllfa & Cwmaman Collieries Limited, a subsidiary of Welsh Associated Collieries Limited. They in turn had acquired Mardy pits in 1932 from Lockets Merthyr Collieries (1894) Limited.

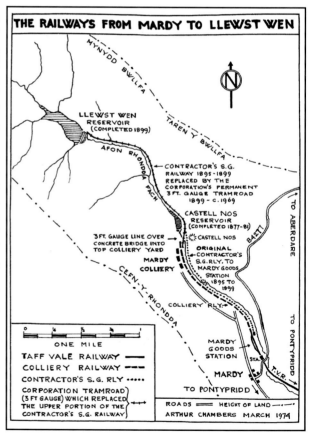

106

*Concrete bridge built by Davies, Middleton & Davies to carry the 3ft gauge tramway from Maerdy colliery to Lluest Wen reservoir. Castell Nos reservoir is just over the brow of the embankment, upper right, 25 May 2004.* *[Geoffrey Hill]*

Immediately above where the Mardy N[os]. 3 & 4 pits were later to stand, the Water Works Company formed a very small reservoir of 20 million gallons at 1,100 ft. above o.d. at grid reference SN 963004; this is called Castell Nos. Work began c.1876 and the dam was newly completed according to a minute of February 1877. This may have been the location where a four-coupled locomotive with the name ZOAR ran on 1ft 11in gauge track for contractor William Jones of Neath. Later in 1886-1888 Jones was to fail to meet his obligations to Cardiff Corporation in respect of Cantref Reservoir (see Chapter 1). Here, too, at Castell Nos it seems probable that the reservoir was not fully commissioned until somewhat later, for by April 1881 and until November 1882 August Krauss, a Bristol contractor, was working at the site.

Krauss is known to have been involved in building filter beds here; this part of his work later became the source of a lengthy claim for payment of £4,700 from the water company (see *Building News*, 6/8/1886). It is possible that he used a 3ft gauge locomotive at the site (see notes on locomotives later) although this is not certain since at this time Krauss was also engaged in building Kennick reservoir in Devon, near Bovey Tracey, for Torquay Local Board of Health.

The Water Works Company subsequently undertook the building of Lluest Wen Reservoir about one mile further up into the head of the valley at grid reference SN 947018 and with a capacity of 242 million gallons and top water level at 1,330 ft. The contract to build this was placed with John Aird and Sons on 29/4/1895, allowing two and a half years for construction, but the reservoir was not

107

completed until 4/1899. Actually it was nearly full by the previous October but Airds were still "pitching" the bank and in the spring of 1899 they did remedial work at one end of the bank. In order to bring up puddle clay, imported by rail over the TVR, Airds built a temporary standard gauge railway from the main line to the site, over a steep and winding route. Steam locomotives would be needed and recollections have been passed down but not identification. The last steep pitch up to the top of the bank would have needed rope haulage.

An unusual feature of this project was that, in view of its inaccessibility, the Water Company decided to have a permanent 3ft gauge railway built to the site. Their engineer reported at 1/5/1899 under the head of "Tramroad" that "the Contractors' 4ft 8½in line has been pulled up and the permanent 3ft rails have been put down as far as the top of the old reservoir". The laying of the permanent line was completed by 16/5/1899. Its ruling gradient was 1 in 44 and there were pitches of 1 in 21, 25, 28 and 29. Recollection is that the Company and the two successor Water Boards made up "bogies" for this line by such expedients as the adaptation of old colliery underground wagons. Their motive power was horses and mules until around 1936, when Davies, Middleton and Davies, contractors of Cardiff, engaged to widen the reservoir spillway at Lluest Wen (for the Taf Fechan Water Supply Board), brought up a 3ft gauge steam locomotive. This was presumably FYLDE. It proved too heavy for the line and created a hazard when its wheels locked descending to the exchange sidings near Mardy colliery. A diesel locomotive was then employed. Perhaps this was owned by the

The only surviving 3ft gauge track on the route to Lluest Wen is this section sunk into the concrete bridge near the Maerdy colliery site 25/5/2004.

*{Geoffrey Hill}*

Water Board since they acquired a new 3ft gauge Ruston & Hornsby 13 hp diesel locomotive in late 1937 and used it as necessary until 1968, at which time the railway was abandoned in favour of road transport. (This locomotive was housed in a shed at grid reference SN 965001.) The contractors also used a standard gauge locomotive, presumably to bring materials from the GWR sidings over the colliery lines to the three-foot gauge interchange.

Photographs, probably taken at the time of the work in the mid-thirties, show the narrow gauge line climbing the steep final bank to the top of the dam, with a bridge over the stream at the foot of this steep pitch and hutments in the yard area created at the foot.

On 12 January 1970 there occurred a much-publicised emergency when the reservoir bank showed signs of failure at a time of winter rains and there was a threat to the safety of the communities down the valley. The alarm was raised when a farmer's horse slipped into a cavity while crossing the dam. Emergency work included the making of an adequate road on the course of the line and M J Gleeson, the contractors, (with Binnies as consultants) undertook extensive work on the bank, renewing its core and topping it in concrete, and on the water channels; this work was completed in 1973.

Most of the narrow gauge tramway was swept away during this work, only a short incline on concrete bridges at the top end of the standard gauge tracks in Mardy colliery yard remained.

## Locomotive used by William Jones at Castell Nos, 1876-1877

*1ft 11in gauge*

ZOAR    0-4-0 (tank?)
     by Sharp Stewart - origin and identity unknown.  Works number 2049, a 1ft 6in gauge engine built in 1870 for the Ebbw Vale Co with 4½in x 6in  cylinders, is a possible contender.

## Locomotive possibly used by August Krauss at Castell Nos, 1881-1882

In the *Colliery Guardian*, 15/7/1881, Krauss of Colston St, Bristol, advertised for "a small locomotive, 3ft gauge, to work upon a tramroad". In *The Engineer* of 18/8/1882 he offered for sale a 3ft gauge contractors loco, 4 wheels coupled, outside cylinders 5in, vertical boiler (Cochran's Patent), weight about 3 tons, little used.  This tiny machine may have been used here or at Krauss's contemporary contract in Devon (or indeed elsewhere). It is interesting to speculate on the builder; Cochran & Co of Annan were boilermakers whilst Cochrane & Co of Middlesbrough are believed to have built at least seven vertical boiler locomotives from c.1863 to c.1880.

## Locomotives used by John Aird at Lluest Wen 1895-1899

Aird did use standard gauge locomotive(s) here but no details are, as yet, available.

STUART, *Manning Wardle 985 of 1887, would seem to have shunted her trucks a little too energetically!  She was used by Davies, Middleton & Davies at Lluest Wen and possibly earlier by Barnes Chaplin & Co at Llwyn-Ddu (see p.119)* [Richard Metcalf Collection]

FYLDE, *Peckett 1671 of 1924, worked rather unsuccessfully on the 3ft gauge for Davies, Middleton & Davies at Lluest Wen. Probably seen here on the earlier Derby Riverlands project with sister engine* HODDER *(Peckett 1672) behind.* *[Frank Jones collection]*

## Locomotives used by Davies, Middleton & Davies at Lluest Wen 1936-8

### Standard gauge

STUART  0-4-0 saddle tank   oc  12in x 18in.
> by Manning Wardle 985 of 1887 - new to T A Walker, contractor, at Liverpool, named MADERO; history not known from 1887 to the 1910s; with Barnes, Chaplin & Co, Cardiff-based contractors, on their Tonypandy watermain contract, Glam, and possibly at Llwyn-Ddu (p.119) c.1911; with P. Baker, the Cardiff engineer and dealer, who affixed 'Rebuilt 1912' plates; to Cardiff Corporation, Grangetown Gasworks, 1914 - c.1936, then to Davies, Middleton and Davies for Lluest Wen; to John Cashmore, Newport Docks, for scrap, c.1938.

### 3ft gauge

FYLDE    0-4-0 side tank   oc  8in x 12in.
> by Peckett 1671 of 1924 - new to Fylde Water Board at their direct labour Stocks Reservoir, W Yorks, contract of 1921 - 1932.  Sold in 9/1932 to Derby Corporation for the Derby Riverlands reclamation scheme. To Harold Potter, the Nottingham dealer, in 1934; later said by HDB to have been with 'Jordan & Co., Caerphilly' (possibly E.C. Jordan & Son, contractors of Newport, working at Caerphilly?). Sold to Davies, Middleton & Davies, whose yard was also at Caerphilly, at some point and used at Lluest Wen, c.1936 - 1938. Seen lying beside GWR Caerphilly Works in 12/1936 and again in 8/1939 (at both times in DMD hands?); they offered a 3ft gauge steam loco for sale in *Machinery Market*, 10/2/1939. To Consett Iron Co. Ltd, Butsfield Limestone Quarry, Co. Durham, 1943; scrapped there in 1951.

- **4wDM    13hp**

by Ruston & Hornsby 187100 of 1937 - new here after 10/1937, the property of Taf Fechan Water Supply Board; used until 1968 when the track was lifted.  To National Museum of Wales, Welsh Industrial & Maritime Museum, Butetown, Cardiff, c.8/1975. Subsequent to the closure of the museum on 31/5/1998 the loco moved to the National Museum of Wales's store at Nantgarw, Glam

## *Llyn Fawr Reservoir*

Llyn Fawr was a natural lake at the foot of the escarpment between Rhigos and the Rhonnda Fawr. Rhondda Urban District Council deemed it suitable for conversion to a reservoir and in 1909 (one year before the formation of the Joint Water Board with Pontypridd) awarded a contract to Henry Lovatt & Company Limited, a Wolverhampton-based firm, to carry out the conversion.  The reservoir site (at grid reference SN 918035) was at a then remote and inaccessible location on the mountain between the Cynon and Rhondda Fawr Valleys (the Rhigos-Treherbert road, now A4061, not having been built at this time).

Initially a six-mile-long railway to the site was promulgated from a junction at Hirwaun Pond (SN 946062) with the GWR Vale of Neath line. This would have been very steeply graded and (of course) with the loads against the gradient. In the event it was decided to move materials to the site by means of an aerial ropeway instead of a railway. The railhead was Llyn Fawr siding at Hirwaun Pond, a short section of the originally proposed railway.  Use by Lovatt of standard gauge locomotive(s) at this railhead is a distinct possibility, as is the use of a railway at the reservoir site.

The reservoir opened in 1914.

# Water for Communities in the Ebbw Vale Area

## *Lower Carno Reservoir for Ebbw Vale Urban District Council*

Water for the use of the Ebbw Vale municipality has long been taken from the formerly Ebbw Vale Steel Company-owned Blaen-y-Cwm Reservoir (described later). The latter eventually came under the administration of the Gwent Water Board based in Newport (and, from April 1974, the Welsh National Water Development Authority), as did reservoirs derived directly from Ebbw Vale UDC and other Monmouthshire councils.

Llangynidr Cwm-yr-Hen, or Upper Carno, Reservoir, of 72 million gallons capacity, was built in 1875-1878 (after a severe drought in 1874) for the Ebbw Vale Local Board of Health.  It was to supply an area from Beaufort and Sirhowy in the north to Aberbeeg in the south. The dam is at grid reference SO 154140 at 1,410ft approximately. As yet no information is available about the contractor on this project or if railways and locomotives were used during construction.

The larger Carno ("a heap or mound"), or Lower Carno, Reservoir (at grid reference SO 164129) has a capacity of 176 million gallons and a top water level at nearly 1,300ft o.d. It was built for Ebbw Vale UDC and officially "opened" on 11 October 1911 by Mr Thomas Morgan, Chairman of the Water Works Committee.  The engineers were George F Deacon Limited and Sir Alexander R Binnie, well known London-based consultants, and the Resident Engineer was Mr H Lawrence Preston.  The contractors were J Hodson and Son Limited of Nottingham and the job ran from c.1905 to 1911. Standard gauge sidings, installed in 1908, adjacent to the Beaufort Sanitary Pipe & Brick Company's works served the site. (Sidings at this location were later used by Nott, Brodie & Company Limited to serve their Blaen-y-Cwm Reservoir site). Narrow gauge tracks ascended its earth embankment during construction and ran along the outer berm - these alignments are clear on a photograph.  It has been recalled that the lines ran away north or northeast from the site to reach a quarry near the mountain road (B4560). This quarry is said to have been at Blaen-Onnen but the quarry mentioned in connection with Blaen-y-Cwm and shown on our map would be much more accessible. Steam motive power seems to have been used on standard, 3ft and 2ft gauges; one locomotive on each!

## Locomotives

All three locomotives were offered for sale by Hodson at Beaufort in 8/1910 (*Western Mail*, 8 and 20/8/1910) and again from Wendover, Bucks, in 2/1912 (*Contract Journal*, 14/2/1912). Finally on 22 and 23/10/1913 (*Contract Journal*, 1/10/1913) an auction sale of plant at Carno included only the Kerr Stuart 2ft gauge locomotive.

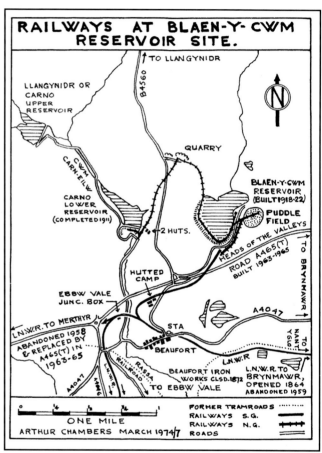

*Standard gauge*

PELLEGRINI      0-6-0 side tank      ic 13in x 18in by Manning Wardle 1006 of 1887 - new to contractor T A Walker at Liverpool; later with Walker's son, C H Walker on his Water Orton contract, Birmingham. At Carno by 1908/1909; to Davies, Middleton & Davies Ltd, the Cardiff-based contractors, on their Cherry Orchard contract for the Rhymney Rly, as GELLI in 1912-1915. It was hired to The Blaenavon Co Ltd during World War I (by whom?) and passed to the Nobel's Explosives Co Ltd by 1919. This company had headquarters in Glasgow, whence equipment and spares were ordered, but it seems likely that the loco may have worked at their factory at Pembrey Burrows, Carmarthenshire, possibly in the construction phase, from 10/1914, and later during the production period.

*3ft gauge*

BROOKE      0-4-0 saddle tank oc 10in x 16in
by Hudswell Clarke 495 of 1898   - new to Huddersfield Corporation, 5/1898, delivered to Butterley Reservoir, Marsden, West Yorks; from 5/1901 with Barnsley Corporation on their Midhope Reservoir project; with Sheffield Corporation from 9/1902 at their Langsett and Underbank Reservoirs scheme in the Little Don Valley, and then back with Huddersfield, c.1904, to work for contractor John Scott on remedial works at the Butterley Reservoir; later with Chesterfield RDC, Derbys; with Hodson by 4/1907 and seemingly used at Carno, since no other major contracts are known for Hodson. Later at Aberthaw & Rhoose Portland Cement & Lime Co. Ltd, Glam, by 1916; later still at H D Pochin & Co. Ltd., St. Dennis Tramway, St. Austell, Cornwall, by 1931; Some sources say that she was finally with contractor Richard Baillie on his Ladybower Reservoir job, Derbys, for Derwent Valley Water Board, 1935-1945, but this is disputed by HDB (none of his informants recalled it) so her final disposal seems to be in doubt.

*2ft gauge*

BEAUFORT  0-4-2 saddle tank  oc 7½in x 12in; a "Tattoo" class engine
by Kerr Stuart 1057 of 1908 - new to Hodson here. Much later at WD, Central Stores Depot
N°.1605, Newbury, Berks, by 5/1920, until at least 1922.  No subsequent information.

Both the Carno reservoirs will have come under the control of the Gwent Water Board as from 1 April 1970.

*A dramatic view of Blaen-y-Cwm reservoir (at left) from the B4560 road heading towards Ebbw Vale, whose ironworks and furnaces are seen under a pall of smoke (centre right) on 22 September 1973.*
*{Harold D Bowtell]*

### Blaen-y-Cwm Reservoir, for Ebbw Vale Steel, Iron and Coal Company Limited

The Ebbw Vale Company occupied a privileged position in wartime and in July 1918 they decided to proceed with the construction of Blaen-y-Cwm (or Beaufort) Reservoir.  The site selected was at grid reference SO 175130, a bare mile north-east of Beaufort township and just to the east of the mountain road, B4560, northward from Beaufort to Llangynidr and Brecon.  An existing reservoir was to be submerged and the new and larger one of 200 million gallons capacity would raise its water level by some 8ft.

The consultants were Sir Alexander Binnie, Son and Deacon, of Westminster, and the contract was placed with Robert Brodie as Executor of L P Nott, the Bristol contractor who had commenced work on Cardiff's Llwynon scheme before 1914.  Construction at Blaen-y-Cwm was sanctioned by the Ebbw Vale Co on 25/7/1918 at an estimated cost of £200,000.  Work began that autumn and was completed in 1922 by which time the contractor's title had changed to Nott, Brodie & Co Ltd.

An earth embankment had to be built, of horseshoe shape in plan and nearly four-fifths of

113

a mile long; only on the north side was no embankment needed as there the ground rose to moorland at over 1,700ft. The top of the bank is at 1,371ft o.d. and top water level at 1,365ft o.d.. A short length of concrete dam was constructed on the east side. Handling of spoil for the embankments involved use of a steam navvy for excavation and a 3ft gauge railway, with locomotives and tip wagons. The embankment foundation trench had to be dug and concrete (involving import of sand and cement by rail) placed in the trench. Clay was found at the site, probably immediately to the east; it was pugged and moved around and placed by rail-mounted steam cranes; in places it was, somewhat unusually, taken down nearly to the rock, with concrete employed only in the immediate foundations. The maximum height of the bank is 53ft and the height from the rock foundations to bank top is 92ft. An unusual piece of equipment was a mechanical punning machine, devised for use in consolidating the dam; from an illustration it is not too clear whether this was steam operated. It may have used compressed air.

*A scene at Ebbw Vale's Blaen-y-Cwm reservoir with the trench for the puddle clay core under construction.* [H D Bowtell Collection]

Stone was quarried near the site, presumably in the small quarry about a quarter mile distant from the northwest corner of the bank and near the B4560 road. There is a probable 3ft gauge formation between the quarry and bank top on a fairly level alignment. This same quarry would very likely have been used by contractors J Hodson & Son Limited building (Lower) Carno Reservoir some ten years earlier. The 3ft gauge railway layout was local to the construction site. It was worked by seven steam locomotives and they had their own engine shed.

Beaufort station (LNWR) was the focal point for inward traffic. This portion of the one-time Merthyr, Tredegar and Abergavenny Railway was opened 1 March 1864, by which time the Company had been leased by the LNWR, which took over ownership in 1866. The station was sandwiched between two road bridges over the line. Just through the westerly bridge (Merthyr/Ebbw Vale direction) a branch curved away northward from the LNWR. This served the Beaufort Sanitary Pipe & Brick Company's works but, more important to our study, it was provided in 1918 with exchange sidings, two roads only, for the reservoir contractor's traffic. (Sidings at this location had earlier, from c.1908, been used by Hodsons building Lower Carno). The branch line was extended, passing huts built for the contactor's workers and under the mountain road just about where today the latter crosses the Heads of the Valleys main road, although at a rather different angle. The private line stopped about 200 yards short of the reservoir, with a run-round loop and engine shed for its two standard gauge locomotives. At this terminal point traffic was transferred to narrow gauge trucks.

The completed Blaen-y-Cwm reservoir suffered from persistent problems of leakage. Its owning company closed the large Ebbw Vale iron and steel works, with a workforce of 4,000, in September/October 1929. The works was completely rebuilt for Richard Thomas & Co Ltd by Sir Robert McAlpine & Sons Ltd during 1936-1938. McAlpines contract included remedial work to Blaen-y-Cwm reservoir in its global cost.

The former LNWR route through Beaufort closed after the last regular passenger trains of Saturday 4 January 1958 and the notable Stephenson Locomotive Society "last train" from Abergavenny to Merthyr and back on 5 January, hauled by "Coal Tank" and "Super D" locomotives (see frontispiece). It is believed, however, that at least nominally access between Ebbw Vale Works, Beaufort and Brynmawr was retained until formal closure from 2 November 1959. Dismantling of the former LNWR tracks in the area took place in 1960 and during the 1960s the Heads of the Valleys Road was constructed, obliterating much of the route of the LNWR and also rendering the course of the Blaen-y-Cwm standard gauge line obscure. The territory between the town of Beaufort and the reservoir is doubly confusing on account of the extent of old workings and tips, no doubt attributable to activities of Joseph and Crawshay Bailey of Nantyglo, whose Beaufort ironworks boasted five blast furnaces by 1838, but which closed in February 1872, the month following the death of Crawshay Bailey.

## Locomotives at Blaen-y-Cwm with the Executor of L P Nott

*Standard gauge*

TRANMERE    0-6-0 saddle tank    oc 13in x 20in
by Hudswell Clarke 654 of 1903 - new to L P Nott, ostensibly at Calvert, Bucks, but used by him on his Cammell Laird contract at Birkenhead (hence the name), c.1903 - 1909, and later on his Cwm Taf (Llwynon) project, c.1910 - c.1916, (see Chapter 2). Then at an ordnance factory in wartime and thence to Beaufort. Subsequently on Nott Brodie's Avonmouth Portway road contract, from 1922, and then at their Shirehampton plant depot, Bristol. Later (1928 - 1930) hired to Edmund Nuttall for his Bartley Reservoir contract, Worcs; before passing to A R Adams, the Newport dealer, after 1932, where we lose trace of her.

PENN    0-6-0 saddle tank    ic 12in x 17in
by Manning Wardle 1539 of 1902 – new to contractors Pauling & Co at Uxbridge on their GC & GW Joint line job, 1902 - 1907, as N°.60 PENN. Hired by Nott, Brodie from the Ebbw Vale Steel, Iron and Coal Co Ltd in c.1920 - 1921; then, in 2/1922, the steel company sold her to the Sheffield Corporation. She worked as PENN at Ewden Waterworks, W. Yorks, 1922 - 1929, (see *Manchester & the Peak*). Later (1931 - 1935) with John Mowlem & Co on their Millbank Graving Dock contract, Southampton, Hants; subsequently on their Chingford Reservoir job, Essex, 1943 - 1947, where she was last seen.

*3ft gauge*

Five of these locomotives have been listed, and their previous histories outlined in detail, in describing the building of the Taf Fechan Reservoir at Pontsticill (see Chapter 3). These arrived at Blaen-y-Cwm in late 1918/early 1919 and were:

| NEWPORT | 0-4-0 saddle tank | oc | 9in x 15in | Hudswell Clarke | 311 of 1889 |
| RUBY | 0-4-0 saddle tank | oc | 8in x 12in | Hudswell Clarke | 424 of 1897 |
| 15 BEAUFORT | 0-4-0 saddle tank | oc | 8in x 12in | Hudswell Clarke | 485 of 1897 |

| LEIGHTON | 0-4-0 saddle tank | oc 10in x 14in | Peckett & Sons | 968 of 1902 |
| REINDEER | 0-4-0 saddle tank | oc 10in x 16in | Hudswell Clarke | 397 of 1892 |

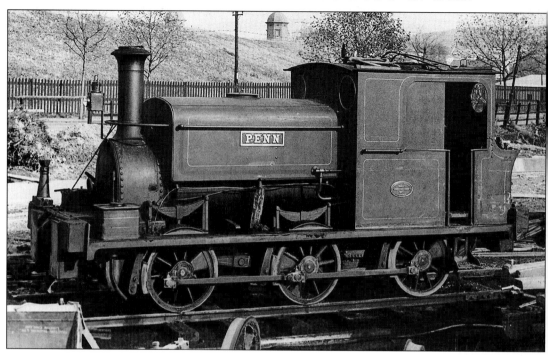

*On hire to the Exor of L P Nott / Nott Brodie for use on the standard gauge at Blaen-y-Cwm was* PENN *(Manning Wardle 1539 of 1902), seen here later on John Mowlem's Chingford reservoir contract, Essex, carrying a 'Rebuilt Yorkshire Engine C°.1931' plate.*     *[George Alliez, ILS Collection]*

The first four of these went on to Pontsticill around June 1922, having been inspected on behalf of the Water Supply Board by J W Price of Treharris on 15 May 1922, and subsequently purchased by the Board on 7 June for £1,900. REINDEER was rejected as being in the poorest condition of the five, but surfaced again in c.1924 as BARNSLEY at Barnsley Corporation's Scout Dike Reservoir, W. Yorks.

Two 0-4-2 tank locomotives by Kerr Stuart were recalled some years ago by Alfred Beck, an old informant of HDB, as working at Blaen-y-Cwm. Both are understood to have gone on to work for Nott, Brodie on the building of the Avonmouth Portway road a year or two after work finished at Beaufort. One may be identified as -

- 0-4-2 saddle tank   oc 9in x 15in  a "Brazil" class engine.
  by Kerr Stuart 4066 of 1920 - new to Robert Brodie at Beaufort, leaving the makers on 19/4/1920. After the Beaufort and Avonmouth Portway contracts she was sold to Dorman Long & Co Ltd at Burley Ironstone Quarries in Rutland. They abandoned their 3ft gauge railway in 1926, replacing it with standard gauge, and rebuilt this loco to standard gauge in 1930. She is said to have been scrapped in 1935.

Blaen-y-Cwm Reservoir will have come under the control of the Gwent Water Board from 1 April 1970.

116

15 BEAUFORT *(Hudswell Clarke 485 of 1897) worked at Blaen-y-Cwm on the 3ft gauge before moving on to Pontsticill (see Chapter 3). She is seen at Consett Iron Co's Butsfield quarry, Co Durham, after WW2 and still carrying the number 15 she had when new at Cyfarthfa.* [Frank Jones]

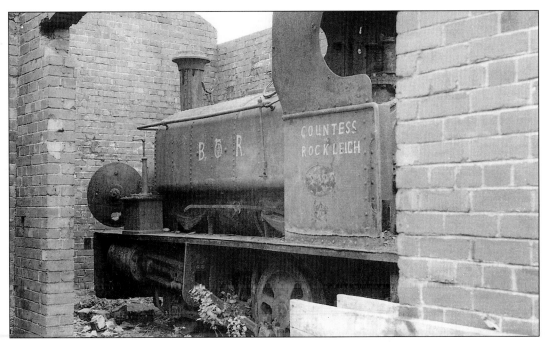

*Hudswell Clarke 311 of 1889, seen here derelict in her storm-battered shed at Porthgain quarry, Pembrokes, was* NEWPORT *when at both Blaen-y-Cwm and Pontsticill.* [Frank Jones]

# Chapter 9

# Notes on other Water Supply
# Projects during the Railway Era

### Cefn Cwrt Reservoir (for Briton Ferry Urban District Council)

Under an agreement dated 19 January 1895, Briton Ferry UDC purchased the very small Ynys-y-Maerdy reservoir (at grid reference SS 750948) from Neath Corporation for £13,000. The rapid industrialization of the area prompted them to promote a much larger reservoir at Cefn Cwrt (dam at grid reference SS 754940). In February 1897 a contract for £16,347 was awarded to contractor James Allen of Cardiff; the first sod was cut on 3 June in the same year by Mr M G Roberts, Chairman of the UDC. The engineer was Mr Tregarnan Rees of Newport and the council's Resident Engineer was Mr H Alex Clarke. The reservoir covers an area of nineteen acres and the top water level is at 882ft o.d. No information is available about the use of railways on this job, though Allen (or Allan) did own at least one locomotive – GWEN (Peckett 801) obtained in September 1899, probably too late to have been used here.

### Cwm Brombil Reservoir (for Port Talbot Docks & Railway Company)

The Port Talbot Docks and Railway Company invited tenders in late 1899/early 1900 for the construction of a private reservoir at Cwm Brombil (grid reference SS 798879) and a water main thence to Port Talbot. The water was to be used to power hydraulic equipment, such as lock gates and cranes, at the docks.

Barnes, Chaplin & Company of Cardiff was the successful bidder. They used a railway (possibly of standard gauge) to bring materials from Taibach to the reservoir site. One locomotive is known to have been used by the contractors. It was a four-coupled Hudswell Clarke tank engine with 10inch cylinders and was offered for sale on 20/7/1904 (*Contract Journal*, 13/7/1904). The identity and subsequent fate of this locomotive is not known.

### Lliedi Reservoirs (for Llanelli local authorities)

The reservoirs are at Felinfoel (renowned for its brewery) in the Lliedi Valley, Dyfed, which was served from 1883 by the Llanelly & Mynydd Mawr Railway.

The Cwm Lliedi Reservoir (at grid reference SN 518032) was authorised by an Act of 1872 and contracts for its construction were let in June 1873 (River Lliedi diversion) and August 1874 (dam). The contractor has not been identified and the use of railways at the site has not been established. An opening ceremony took place on 17 September 1878.

Llanelly Urban District Council invited tenders for the Upper Lliedi Reservoir (SN 513043) in 1899. Louis P. Nott, later involved in the construction of Llwynon (see Ch. 2) and Blaen-y-Cwm (see Ch. 8) Reservoirs, put in the successful bid of £38,000 and began work in May 1900. A standard gauge siding connected the site with the nearby L&MM railway and at least one locomotive used by Nott at the site has been identified. This was LLIEDI, which only arrived in September 1902 suggesting the possibility of other, unknown engines at the site - certainly in the 1900 - 1902 period. (It is significant to note that Nott's colleague Robert Brodie was supervising at Lliedi and also at the nearby North Dock construction project, Llanelli, (for the Llanelly Harbour Trust), which was also using locomotives, 1898-1903.) Work at the reservoir would seem to have been completed by c.1904.

### Standard gauge locomotive used at Upper Lliedi

LLIEDI     0-4-0 saddle tank   oc 12in x 18in
> by Hunslet 199 of 1879 - new to Mountsorrel Granite Co Ltd, Leics, their WILLIE; to Nott, at Lliedi presumably, from Hunslet's works 25/9/1902; later at Nott's Princess Risborough - Grendon Underwood (GWR/GCR Joint) contract, Bucks, by 14/5/1904; later still, between 9/1907 and 3/1913, to Buchanan's Flour Mills Ltd, Seacombe, Ches, their SILVER QUEEN. She was still at Seacombe in 7/1929 but disappeared sometime later.

### *Llwyn-Ddu Reservoir (for Abergavenny Urban District Council)*

This is a very small reservoir in the Brecon Beacons National Park just north-west of the town at grid reference SO 290159. It was built in 1913 to capture the waters of the Cibbi springs. Details are uncertain but the Cardiff contractor Barnes, Chaplin & Co is said to have had a waterworks contract at Abergavenny at this time using the standard gauge locomotive listed here. If this was the case, the site would have been served by a siding from the LNWR Abergavenny – Merthyr Tydfil line some ¾ mile distant. The locomotive is:

STUART     0-4-0 saddle tank   oc 12in x 18in
> by Manning Wardle  985 of 1887 – new to T A Walker, contractor, at Liverpool, named MADERO. No further history until with Barnes, Chaplin, c.1911 on their Tonypandy - Blaenclydach watermain contract (for Rhondda UDC?) and here. To P Baker, the Cardiff engineer and dealer, who affixed 'Rebuilt 1912' plates; to Cardiff Corporation, Grangetown gasworks, 1914-1936, then to Davies, Middleton & Davies' contract for Lluest Wen Reservoir (see page 110 for this and the locomotive's later disposal, with an illustration on page 109).

GYP *(Andrew Barclay 761 of 1895) may have been used by P & W Anderson on a contract at Llwyn-Ddu reservoir, Abergavenny around 1925. Seen here on the same contractors' earlier North Devon & Cornwall Junction Light Railway contract.*       *[Peter Michie Collection]*

It is also suggested that contractor P & W Anderson Ltd had a contract at Abergavenny waterworks, possibly c.1925, and that a 3ft gauge Andrew Barclay locomotive GYP, ex Anderson's North Devon & Cornwall Junction Light Railway contract, was used on this job. Details of Anderson's contract are even more vague than that of Barnes, Chaplin. Further information on either would be most welcome. The known history of this locomotive is:

GYP        0-4-0 side tank    oc 6in x 12in
    by Andrew Barclay 761 of 1895 - new to Morrison & Mason Ltd for Bradford's Haden Carr reservoir construction and transferred in 1898 to the Elan Valley pipeline (Dolau to Hagley), then about 1903 sent to Scotland for work on the Maidens & Dunure Light Railway. By 5/1908 had been sold to contractor Sir John Jackson Ltd at Kinlochleven on the reservoir and hydro-electric scheme for British Aluminium Co Ltd, completed in 1910. Included in the plant sale at Jackson's Grays Depôt 8/1921. Acquired by P & W Anderson after 10/1922. Later to A R Adams, the Newport dealer, by 1/1927.

### *Moss House Wood Reservoir (for Neath Urban District Council)*

James Allen (or Allan), the Cardiff-based contractor who built Briton Ferry's Cefn Cwrt Reservoir (see p.118), won this earlier contract for the 25 million gallon Moss House Wood Reservoir, near Neath in 1896. The dam was at SS 777981, about half a mile due south of Tonna village. The opening took place in June 1898. The use of railways at the site has not been established.

NORAH *(Manning Wardle 997 of 1887, a classic 'D' class engine) worked for Thomas Taylor on his Western Valleys water and sewerage contract of which little is known. The locomotive is shown later in life at the Treforest Tinplate Co Ltd's works, Glamorgan.*        *[Frank Jones Collection]*

## Rhymney Bridge Waterworks
### (for the Western Valleys Sewerage Board?)

Thomas Taylor of Pontypridd carried out a contract to construct "Western Valley Sewers and Rhymney Bridge Waterworks" which was completed in 1908. (At that time the River Rhymney formed the Monmouthshire/Glamorgan county boundary in the northern part of the Rhymney valley, so attributing the project to a county is difficult. However in the post-1974 boundaries much of the works must fall in Glamorgan.)

At the closing auction sale on 11 August 1908 "at Rhymney Bridge, St. Brides and Bassaleg.... two four-coupled tank locomotives 9in and 10in by Manning Wardle and Hunslet" were offered (*Contract Journal,* 29/7/1908, and *Machinery Market,* 31/7/1908). One of these has been tentatively identified as:

NORAH     0-4-0 saddle tank   oc 8in x 14in (note cylinder size)
    by Manning Wardle 997 of 1886 - new to Geen & Parker, contractors of Cardiff; then with W H Mathias of Pontypridd on his Cowbridge & Aberthaw Railway contract for the Taff Vale Railway, until 1892. To Taylor at a date unknown. After the closing auction here in 1908 she was with Arthur Morgan of Newport by c.1912; later with Treforest Tinplate Co Ltd at Treforest, Mid Glam, until disposed of at some time after 1932.

It is of interest to note that contractors William Underwood & Brother of Dukinfield, Cheshire, (see Chapters 5 and 6) are also said to have carried out work for the Western Valleys Sewerage Board sometime between 1900 and 1909. No further details are available.

## Sion Sheffrey's Reservoir for the Tredegar Iron Co;
### (later to Tredegar Urban District Council)

This reservoir at Nantybwch, dam at grid reference SO 130115, was built from c.1863 to "the early part of 1865" by the Tredegar Iron Company to provide for domestic supply in that town. No information has yet come to light concerning the contractor involved or the use of railways during construction at this relatively early date, but this must be a possibility given the close proximity of two railways to the site. The first was the iron company's long-established 2ft 11in gauge locomotive-worked tramplate line from the ironworks to Trefil limestone quarries. This line passed within less than 500 yards of easy terrain from the site of the dam. A second nearby railway was the Merthyr, Tredegar & Abergavenny line of the London & North Western Railway striking westwards along the heads of the valleys from Abergavenny. The Brynmawr – Nantybwch section opened to traffic on 1 March 1864, well before the reservoir was completed.

Both Llwyn-Ddu and Sion Sheffrey's Reservoirs will have come under the control of the Gwent Water Board from 1 April 1970.

# *Acknowledgments*

H arold Bowtell spent as many as 30 years gathering the material for this book. One of the joys for him of such a task was the opportunity the project provided for making friends amongst people, in the locality and elsewhere, who remembered the events depicted in the text. Numerous fellow railway historians also gave freely of the results of their researches. Below, I have listed those whose names appear in Harold's research notes. There are doubtless many others who helped in a variety of ways and whose names I do not know. I hope they will accept my apologies. Equally truly many of the people listed here must, sadly, no longer be with us: --

Eric Armstrong, Allan C Baker, Fred Ball, Alfred Beck, Vic Bradley, Fred Davies, J Max Dunn, Dan Evans, Richard Evans, William Ferguson, John Fletcher, Lionel Heath, Harry Hicken, D Hughes, Geoffrey Horsman, John B Horne, Trevor Lodge, Sid Morgan, Islwyn Owens, Harry Paar, Jack Phillips, Ken Plant, Martin Potts, G F Roberts, Peter Rowbotham, Mathias Thomas, Ted Thomas, Rev David Tipper, Mr Wharton (Wentwood), Tom Williams.

Grateful thanks are also due to the staffs of the following public authorities and water companies:

*Cardiff Corporation* (A S Riley, Donald Coke, Bryn Davies, Mr Muggeridge, George Nicholas, F J R Potter, John Wild). *Taf Fechan Water Board* (D G Gamblin, Mr Lewis, D G Rowlands, Idris Thomas, Mr Walters). *West Glamorgan Water Board* (R J Lillicrap, Bernard Harker). *Gwent Water Board* (A E Guild, Percy Beard, Reg Dyer, Mr Hughes [Talybont Superintendent], J Lamey, Jack Lowlin, Mr Thomas, L W J Nash). *The Glamorgan County Record Office, Cardiff. The Gwent (Monmouthshire) County Record Office, Cwmbran. Ebbw Vale Library* (Miss Colwell). *Pontypridd Library* (R W Davies, Mr Angus).

The following railway societies must be thanked for supplying much information:

The Narrow Gauge Railway Society
The Industrial Locomotive Society and its journal *The Industrial Locomotive*
The Industrial Railway Society and *The Industrial Railway Record*
The Stephenson Locomotive Society and its *Journal*

The late Arthur Chambers collaborated with HDB in fieldwork and prepared many of the maps and Douglas Rendell copied or prepared many of the illustrations collected by HDB. The following people and organizations kindly offered assistance to the present co-author:

Michael Blackmore, Chris Barber (of *Blorenge Books*), Bob Darvill, Roger Hateley, John van Laun, Ian Pope, Clive Walters (NGRS), *Aberdare Library* (Alun Prescott), *Newport Library* (Alun Prescott, again), *Neath Library* (Annette Jones), *Tredegar Library* (Janet Karn), *West Glamorgan County Archives, Swansea,* (Sarah Phillips), *Dwr Cymru Welsh Water* (Julian Rabjohn & Brian Nelson); Mr Rabjohn and *Dwr Cymru Welsh Water* kindly allowed the use of photographs from *The Talybont Saga. Abergavenny Museum, Monmouthshire County Council* (Rachael Rogers and staff) were similarly gracious in making available copyright photographs of Grwyne Fawr reservoir from the David Tipper collection.

Moya Rayner retyped Harold's unscannable first-draft typescript and copied it to disk, thus making my task vastly easier. Allan C Baker, Ted Gray, Frank Jones and Peter Michie gave invaluable help with photographs. Roger Hateley kindly provided additional maps. Michael Blackmore has allowed me to reproduce his route map of the Grwyne Fawr transport links and also three associated layout diagrams. Barry Lane painted the picture chosen for the jacket. Fellow ILS members Allen Civil, Peter Michie, Bob Miller, Peter Rowbotham and John K Williams have been through the manuscript and made useful suggestions. Bob Miller also compiled the index and laid out the book for the printer and Douglas Robinson digitally enhanced a number of the photographs. I am very grateful to all of them. Finally, my wife, Rosemary Bradley, has been a source of computer expertise and of tolerant and good-humoured support throughout.

GH, 10/2005

# INDEX

# LOCOMOTIVE OWNERS' INDEX

This index lists also all the previous and subsequent owners, as well as hirers, dealers and agents, as given in the locomotive histories.

The maintenance men of the Abertillery and District Water Board at the Grwyne Fawr workshops about 1926 (see Ch. 6); the dirty conditions prevailing led them to become known as the 'Black Gang'. [© Abergavenny Museum, Monmouthshire County Council]

# LOCOMOTIVE BUILDERS' INDEX

I L S

128

# OTHER PUBLICATIONS OF THE SOCIETY

## CONTRACTORS' STEAM LOCOMOTIVES OF SCOTLAND

### by Russell Wear & Michael Cook

Every steam locomotive operated by contractors in Scotland,
with details of the contracts undertaken.   An invaluable record.

**134 *A5 size* pages** * **loose leaf format** * **card covers** * **£6.00 post free**

\*   \*   \*   \*   \*   \*   \*

## CONTRACTORS' LOCOMOTIVES
## PART VII                    by Bob Miller

Details all the locomotives operated and the contracts undertaken
by these nine public works' contractors:-

**James Byrom  *  Thomas Docwra  *  Holloway Brothers**

**McGregor & Badman  *  Morrison & Mason**

**Sir Lindsay Parkinson  *  Enoch Tempest**

**Topham, Jones & Railton  *  Thomas Wrigley**

**44 *A5 size* pages** * **17 photographs** * **card covers** * **£6.00 post free**

*OR BOTH THE ABOVE BOOKS TOGETHER FOR £10 post free*

ooooOOOOOOOoooo

## STEAM LOCOMOTIVES IN INDUSTRY  1930-50

### by John K Williams & Bob Miller

97 vintage photographs with extended captions

**64 *A5 size* pages**       *       **paperbacked**       *       **£6.00 post free**

# OTHER PUBLICATIONS OF THE SOCIETY

## DETAILED LOCOMOTIVE WORKS LISTS

for the following firms with every engine classified and first owner shown, also with a brief history of the locomotive builders. Card covers

---

### KERR STUART & Co Ld

by Frank Jux    *    48 *A4 size* pages    *    £6.35 inc. postage

---

### BLACK, HAWTHORN & Co and
### CHAPMAN & FURNEAUX

by Allan C Baker    *    42 *A4 size* pages    *    £4.60 inc. postage

---

### JOHN FOWLER & Co

by Frank Jux    *    58 *A4 size* pages    *    £6.35 inc. postage

---

### BAGNALLS OF STAFFORD

by Allan C Baker and Allen Civil   *   42 *A4 size* pages   *   £5.20 inc. postage

---

### PECKETT & SONS

by Frank Jux    *    38 *A4 size* pages    *    £5.20 inc. postage

---

## The Industrial Locomotive Society

was founded in 1937 to cater for everyone interested in locomotives operated by industrial concerns, such as the public works' contractors listed in this book, and their environment. Members receive the Society's Journal *The Industrial Locomotive* four times per annum and have access to a well-stocked specialist library. Further details may be obtained from the Society web site:

www.industrial-loco.org.uk

or from the Hon. Publications and Sales Officer - David Embling,
77 Station Crescent, Rayleigh, Essex. SS6 8AR
e-mail: davidembling@btconnect.com

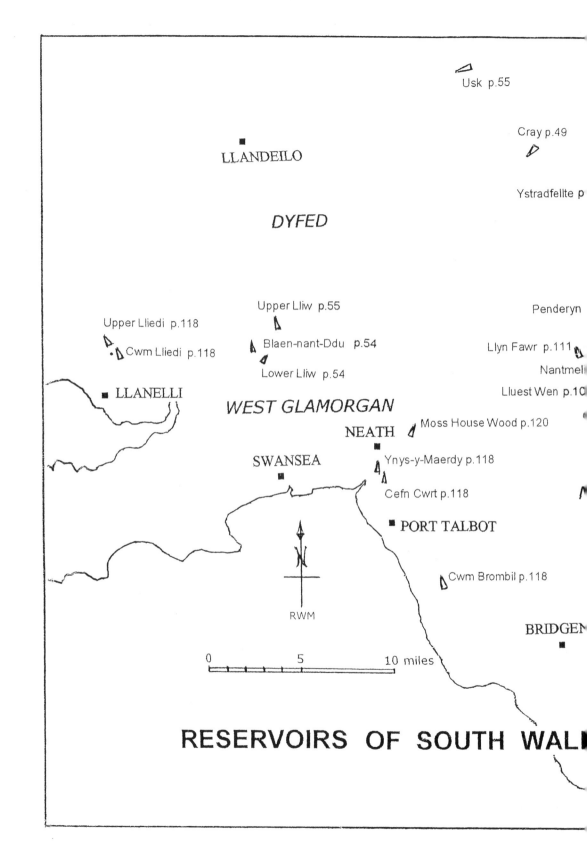

Usk p.55

Cray p.49

Ystradfellte p

LLANDEILO

DYFED

Upper Lliw p.55

Penderyn

Upper Lliedi p.118

Blaen-nant-Ddu  p.54

Llyn Fawr p.111

Cwm Lliedi p.118

Nantmel

Lower Lliw  p.54

Lluest Wen p.10

LLANELLI

WEST GLAMORGAN

Moss House Wood p.120

NEATH

SWANSEA

Ynys-y-Maerdy p.118

Cefn Cwrt p.118

PORT TALBOT

Cwm Brombil p.118

RWM

BRIDGEN

0        5        10 miles

RESERVOIRS OF SOUTH WAL